Workbook

Achievers

Helen Halliwell

A2

Richmond

Contents

For audio, go to **richmondelt.com/achievers/studentaudio**

Starter A

VOCABULARY Numbers Classroom objects

1 Write the numbers.

1 6 ______ 2 22 ______
3 90 ______ 4 14 ______
5 100 ______ 6 55 ______

2 Write the number of …

1 days in July. ______
2 months in a year. ______
3 letters in *workbook*. ______
4 days in a year. ______

3 Write the words in the box under the correct heading.

book clock computer folder pen
picture rubber scissors whiteboard

in a pencil case	on a desk	on a classroom wall

4 Complete the words with the vowels.

1 
ch _ _ r

2 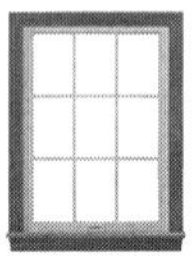
w _ nd _ w

3 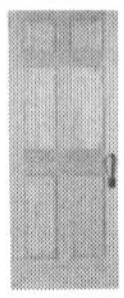
d _ _ r

4 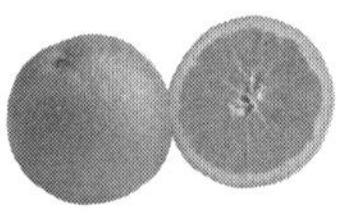
_ r _ ng _

5 
_ mbr _ ll _

6 
c _ lc _ l _ t _ r

GRAMMAR *a / an* *this / that / these / those*

5 Look at the words in exercise 4. Write *a* or *an* for each one.

1 ______ 2 ______
3 ______ 4 ______
5 ______ 6 ______

6 Complete the sentences with *this* or *these*.

1 ______ is my classroom. It's 5B.
2 ______ is my pencil case.
3 ______ are my pencils.
4 ______ are my scissors.
5 ______ is my workbook.
6 ______ are my two rubbers.

7 Complete the dialogue with *that* or *those*.

Joe: 1 ______ are my books and 2 ______ are my folders.
Alexa: Is 3 ______ your pencil case?
Joe: No, 4 ______'s Tom's.
Alexa: Are 5 ______ your pencils?
Joe: Yes, but 6 ______ aren't my scissors.

CHECK

8 Look at the picture and circle the correct words in the dialogue.

Teacher: Whose is 1 **this / that** 2 **rubber / ruler**?
Rafa: 3 **This / That**'s mine.
Teacher: And whose are 4 **these / those** 5 **pens / pencils**?
Leila: 6 **These / Those** are mine.
Teacher: OK. Let's start the lesson. There's 7 **a / an** picture on the wall. What is it?
Grace: It's 8 **a / an** orange.

Starter B

VOCABULARY Days and months, Ordinal numbers | Dates

1 Write the days of the week in order.

1 *Monday*
2 ______
3 ______
4 ______
5 ______
6 ______
7 ______

2 Complete the text with the correct months.

In the northern hemisphere, the three months of Spring are March, 1 ______ and 2 ______. Summer is in 3 ______, July and 4 ______. Autumn starts in 5 ______ and finishes in 6 ______. Then, the three months of Winter are December, 7 ______ and 8 ______.

3 Complete the sentences with the ordinal numbers in words.

1 The ______ month of the year is October.
2 The ______ month of the year is July.
3 The ______ letter of the alphabet is *n*.
4 The ______ letter of the alphabet is *e*.
5 The person in ______ place gets a gold medal in the Olympics.
6 In the Olympics, the person in ______ place gets a bronze medal.

4 How do you say these dates? Write them in words.

1 06/08 *Sixth of August*
2 27/06 ______
3 19/11 ______
4 01/02 ______
5 30/04 ______
6 12/09 ______

GRAMMAR *be*, Subject and object pronouns

5 Complete the text with the correct affirmative or negative form of the verb *be*.

Sarah 1 ______ my best friend. Our birthdays 2 ______ on the same day, 10th September, but we 3 ______ the same age. Sarah 4 ______ one year older than me. She 5 ______ 14 now, but I 6 ______ 14 until next year. I 7 ______ 13 now.

6 Complete the table with the missing subject and object pronouns.

Subject pronouns	Object pronouns
I	1 *me*
2	you
he	3
4	her
it	5
6	us
they	7

7 Circle the correct words in the exchanges.

Andrea: 1 **He / She / It**'s my sister's birthday today. 2 **He / She / It**'s 18.
Joe: Say 'Happy birthday' from 3 **me / him / her**.

Sheila and Ben: Can you help 4 **you / him / us**? What's 83 x 32. We don't know the answer.
Bart: 5 **I / He / It**'s 2656.
Sheila and Ben: Thank 6 **us / you / them**!

Basil: Who are those two people? I don't know 7 **they / them / her**.
Bea: The boy is called Paolo. 8 **He / She / It**'s nice. I like 9 **it / him / her**. I'm not sure who the girl is.

CHECK

8 Complete the text with the words in the box.

are aren't February he him it (x2) 's tenth 40th

Every four years, there 1 ______ 365 days in a year. There 2 ______ 366. That's because 3 ______'s a leap year and there 4 ______ an extra day. My dad was born on 29th 5 ______. It's strange for 6 ______ because for three years he celebrates his birthday on the 28th. Then, in a leap year, he celebrates 7 ______ on the correct day. How old is 8 ______ on that day? For example, this year, it's his 9 ______ year, but it's only his 10 ______ birthday!

Starter C

VOCABULARY Animals | The alphabet

1 Complete the animals with the vowels.

1 p_rr_t
2 t_g_r
3 _nt
4 d_lph_n
5 wh_l_
6 p_g__n
7 _l_ph_nt
8 b_tt_rfly

2 Write the words in exercise 1 under the correct heading.

no legs	two legs

four legs	six legs

3 Put the letters below into the correct group.

D I K N U

A	T	L	Y	Q

GRAMMAR *have got* | Possessives

4 Rewrite the sentences in the affirmative (+), negative (–) or interrogative form (?).

1 I've got a big family.
(–) ______
2 They haven't got a cat.
(?) ______
3 Has it got four legs?
(+) ______
4 You haven't got a computer.
(?) ______
5 She's got an orange ruler.
(–) ______
6 Ana and Lara haven't got a book.
(+) ______

5 Rewrite the sentences with a possessive adjective or 's to indicate possession.

1 Those shoes belong to him.
They're ______ shoes.
2 This bag belongs to me.
It's ______ bag.
3 That hamster belongs to me and my family.
It's ______ hamster.
4 These scissors belong to them.
They're ______ scissors.
5 That bike belongs to my friend.
It's my ______ bike.
6 Those pencils belong to Ana.
They're ______ pencils.

6 Read the sentences. Write the number of the sentence under the correct heading in the table.

1 Marta**'s** dog, Bob, is black.
2 He**'s** ten years old.
3 Bob**'s** kennel is in the garden.
4 It**'s** got two windows.
5 Marta**'s** got pictures of Bob on her phone.
6 Bob**'s** her favourite animal.

's = is	's = has	's = possession

CHECK

7 Complete the text with the words in the box.

have got   have you got   its   pet
's got   their   've got   wild animal

[1] ______ any idea what this is? It's a *Daubentonia madagascariensis*, but it [2] ______ another name, the aye-aye. It's a [3] ______ and it lives in the rainforests of Madagascar. It isn't a [4] ______. Aye-ayes [5] ______ small eyes, but [6] ______ ears are very big. They [7] ______ long fingers, too. An aye-aye uses [8] ______ very long middle finger to get food.

Starter D

VOCABULARY Colours | Clothes

1 Reorder the letters and write the colours.

1 lewoyl ____________________
2 tweih ____________________
3 pkni ____________________
4 ebul ____________________
5 klabc ____________________
6 ornbw ____________________
7 luprep ____________________

2 Complete the table with the colours in exercise 1.

white	+	red	=	[1]
[2]	+	yellow	=	green
blue	+	red	=	[3]
[4]	+	white	=	grey
red	+	green	=	[5]
blue	+	[6]	=	light blue
[7]	+	red	=	orange

3 Complete the words with the vowels.

1 You wear s_ngl_ss_s when it's sunny.
2 You wear tr__n_rs for sport.
3 You wear __rr_ngs in your ears.
4 You wear a n_ckl_c_ around your neck.
5 My mum wears tr__s_rs for work.
6 You wear a j_mp_r in winter.
7 You wear a c_p on your head.

4 Complete the words.

1 
w___h

2 
s___s

3 
h___y

4 
s___t

5 
d___s

6 
s___f

7 
j___s

8 
j____t

GRAMMAR Plurals | *there is / there are*

5 Write the plurals of the words in exercise 4. Use *s*, *es*, *ies*, *ves* or *pairs of*.

1 ____________________
2 ____________________
3 ____________________
4 ____________________
5 ____________________
6 ____________________
7 ____________________
8 ____________________

6 Complete the dialogue with *is*, *isn't*, *are* or *aren't*.

Beth: There [1] ____________ two beds in my bedroom, one for me and one for my brother. There [2] ____________ also a big desk.
Brad: [3] ____________ there any books on it?
Beth: No, there [4] ____________, but there [5] ____________ some books on the floor.
Brad: [6] ____________ there a computer on the desk?
Beth: Yes, there [7] ____________. There [8] ____________ a new one and it's great.
Brad: There [9] ____________ a chest of drawers in our room, but it's OK because there [10] ____________ a big wardrobe. It's full of our clothes!

CHECK

7 Circle the correct words in the phone conversation.

Paula: Alisha, [1] **is / are** there a hoody in your bedroom?
Alisha: Let's see ... there are two [2] **hoodys / hoodies**. There's a [3] **red / dark** blue one.
Paula: That's Clare's.
Alisha: And there [4] **'s / are** a red one. There [5] **is / are** three dolphins on it.
Paula: That's my hoodie!
Alisha: OK.
Paula: [6] **Is / Are** there any sunglasses on your chest of drawers?
Alisha: Yes, [7] **are there / there are**. There are two [8] **pair / pairs**, but one pair is mine.
Paula: The others are mine!

1 It's my life

READING

1 Read the webpage. What is it about?

A Accommodation B Families
C Free time activities D Jobs

2 Which advert is in American English?

HOME FINDER

HOME SEARCH CONTACT

1 STUDIO FLAT
In the heart of the city and close to shops, cafés and the underground. A large living room / bedroom with a sofa bed and cooking facilities, and a small bathroom. No pets.

2 GARDEN FLAT
A one bedroom flat on the ground floor. A modern kitchen and bathroom, large living room and private garden. Two minutes from the Emirates Stadium – perfect for football fans!

3 APARTMENT
On the top floor of a modern apartment building very close to the business district. Two bedrooms, a large living room and balcony. Private elevator and space in private parking lot.

4 HOUSE
A two bedroom house in a quiet neighbourhood 30 minutes from the centre of the city. Small front garden. Close to a large park and the motorway into the city.

5 HOUSE
A four bedroom house with a big back garden and a small studio flat – a great place for guests or an elderly relative. Good shops and restaurants nearby, including Westfield shopping centre.

3 These people want to find somewhere to live. Read the webpage again and match A–E with 1–5.

A 
Tom and Lisa have got three teenagers. Lisa's mother lives with them too. Tom has got an office in the business district and likes good food.

B 
Edith lives alone with her two cats, Minnie and Max. She's interested in trees and flowers, and she doesn't like lifts.

C 
Matt and Sally both work in the business district. Matt likes football and fast cars. He's got a Porsche Spyder. Sally prefers shopping.

D 
Leo is a student at university in the centre of the city. He plays rugby, but he hates football. He hasn't got a car.

E 
Richard and Emma have got two young children and a dog. They don't like life in the city. They prefer nature.

4 Match 1–6 with A– F.

EXTRA WORD ZONE

British and American English

1 the underground	A mall
2 football	B the subway
3 block of flats	C parking lot
4 car park	D soccer
5 motorway	E freeway
6 shopping centre	F apartment building

1 ___ 2 ___ 3 ___ 4 ___ 5 ___ 6 ___

5 Rewrite advert 4 on the webpage in exercise 2 in American English.

VOCABULARY Family

6 Complete the puzzle.

1 The man married to your mother, but not your father.
2 Another word for father.
3 Another word for mother.
4 A female sibling.
5 An ... child hasn't got any siblings.
6 The plural of child.
7 Your mother and father are your ... .
8 A ... and wife.

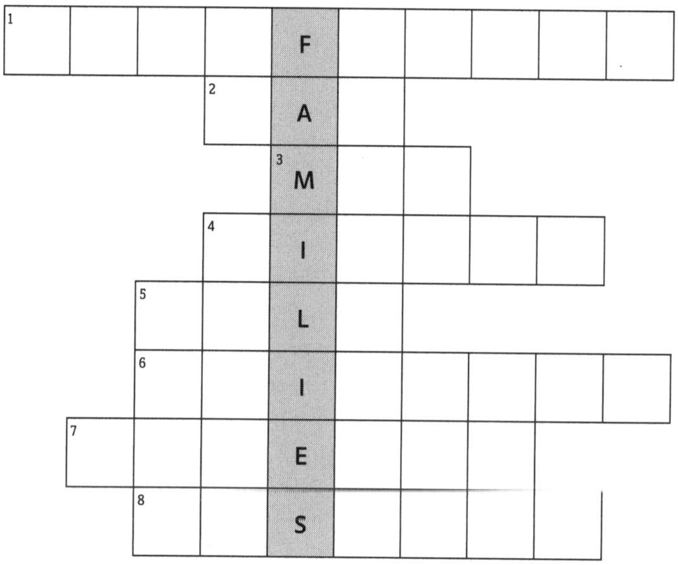

7 Rewrite the sentences using one word instead of the words in bold.

1 Sam is my **sister's son**.
____

2 His **dad's father** is ninety.
____

3 Their **mum's grandparents** aren't alive.
____

4 I like my **dad's sister**.
____

5 I've got the same name as my **mum's mother**.
____

6 They haven't got a **female child**.
____

7 Our **aunt and uncle's children** live in the USA.
____

8 Is Sue your **brother's daughter**?
____

WANT TO KNOW MORE?
Stages in life

8 Match sentences 1–3 with photos A–C. Use a dictionary if you need to.

1 Ray and Jo are **middle-aged**. They've got two children. One is a **young adult** and one is a **teenager**.
2 Amy is a **schoolchild**, but her little brother Tom is only a **toddler**.
3 Jack is quite **elderly**. His grandchild is only a **baby**.

9 Write the words in bold in exercise 8 in chronological order. Start with the youngest.

1 ________ 2 ________ 3 ________
4 ________ 5 ________ 6 ________
7 ________

10 Complete the dialogue with six of the words in exercise 9.

Joel: Is that your sister in the photo?
Nick: No, it isn't. My sister is thirteen. She's a [1]________ .
Joel: Who's that, then?
Nick: That's my niece. She's one and a half so she's a [2]________ . And that's my nephew. He's six so he's a [3]________ now.
Joel: And is that your uncle?
Nick: No, that's my grandpa! He's only 51 so he's [4]________ . He isn't [5]________ like a lot of grandparents.
Joel: What's that noise?
Nick: That's my stepbrother. He's a [6]________ . He's only two months old!

11 Write sentences about people in your family. Include their relation to you, their age and their stage in life.

Yolanda is my sister. She's six months old. She's a baby.
____
____
____
____
____

GRAMMAR Present simple

1 Complete the texts with the affirmative or negative form of the verbs.

carry come go like play practise walk win

This is Thierry Brown. His first name is French, but he [1] ________ from France. He's from a small town near Oxford. Thierry [2] ________ to school in his town. It isn't far from his house so he [3] ________ there and back every day. On Tuesdays and Thursdays he [4] ________ walking because he [5] ________ a musical instrument on those days. It's a saxophone and it's heavy! Thierry is good at music and he [6] ________ his saxophone in the school jazz band. They [7] ________ twice a week and they often [8] ________ music competitions.

live have got work come think see use teach

These are Thierry's sisters. They [9] ________ English names either. There's Liesel (that's German) and Chiara (that's Italian). Their parents obviously [10] ________ that English names are boring! Liesel and Chiara [11] ________ at home any more. Liesel is at university in London, and Chiara [12] ________ as a teacher in Brighton. She [13] ________ English to foreign students. The girls are very busy and they [14] ________ home often, but they [15] ________ their parents every few days. How do they do that? They [16] ________ FaceTime!

2 Write true sentences about Thierry's family.

1 Thierry and his parents / live / in England
____

2 Thierry / go / to school by bus
____

3 He / play / a musical instrument
____

4 Liesel / has got / an Italian name
____

5 Mr and Mrs Brown / like / English names
____

6 Chiara / work / in an office
____

3 Complete the questions with *Do* or *Does* and write full answers.

1 ________ Thierry go to school in France?
____

2 ________ his parents drive him to school?
____

3 ________ some students play in a jazz band?
____

4 ________ Liesel live in Oxford?
____

5 ________ Chiara teach Italian?
____

6 ________ Mr and Mrs Brown use FaceTime?
____

4 Write the questions and complete the exchanges.

you / what time / do / in the morning / get up
to / school / you / do / get / how
does / lesson / the first /when / start
study / why / you / do / history
dad / does / work / where / your
what / you / like / do / in / doing / your free time

1 **Brandon:** ________?
Camilla: Because I'm interested in the past.

2 **Tim:** ________?
Bruce: I like cooking and watching cooking programmes on TV.

3 **Cathy:** ________?
Daphne: It starts at 8.45.

4 **Darius:** ________?
Adam: At my school. He teaches maths.

5 **Duke:** ________?
Emma: At about half past seven, but my alarm clock rings at seven!

6 **Etta:** ________?
Gill: I walk or cycle.

5 Write true answers for you to the questions in exercise 4.

1 ________
2 ________
3 ________
4 ________
5 ________
6 ________

LISTENING

1 Complete the definitions with the words in the box. Use a dictionary if you need to.

computer-literate computer programmer computer science game designer gamer screen software

1 ________________, *n.* The study of computers.

2 ________________, *n.* A person who plays computer games.

3 ________________, *n.* The programs used by a computer.

4 ________________, *adj.* Able to use a computer.

5 ________________, *n.* A person who writes programs for a computer.

6 ________________, *n.* The part of a computer where the information appears.

7 ________________, *n.* A person who plans what happens in a computer game.

2 (2) Listen and choose the correct words in the summary.

It's [1] **a quiz / an article / an interview**. It's [2] **on the radio / on TV / in a computer games magazine**. It's about a [3] **computer science teacher / computer programmer / games designer** called Jake.

3 (2) Listen again and tick (✓) the correct box.

1 *Top Games* is for people interested in … .
A Science ☐
B sport ☐
C computer games ☐

2 Jake says that … .
A his job is really important ☐
B his age doesn't matter ☐
C his age is very important ☐

3 Mario and Luigi are Jake's … .
A pets ☐
B parents ☐
C brothers ☐

4 Jake explains that he … .
A finishes his homework and then starts work ☐
B does some work and then does his homework ☐
C doesn't do his homework ☐

5 Jake's inspiration is from things that … .
A he does with his friends ☐
B he studies at school ☐
C he watches and reads ☐

6 Jake's computer programmer is … .
A one of his teachers ☐
B one of his friends ☐
C someone he doesn't know ☐

TEST YOUR MEMORY!

4 Circle T (true) or F (false). Then correct the false sentences.

1 Jake is fourteen. T / F
2 His hometown is Brighton. T / F
3 His pets are dogs. T / F
4 He goes to school on foot. T / F
5 His bedroom is his office. T / F
6 He wants to work in Australia in the future. T / F

____
____
____

5 Write these exchanges in your language.

1 Thanks for coming today.

____

No worries.

____

2 Can you tell us about yourself?

____

Sure.

____

1

READING

1 Read the article quickly. Which two topics in the box aren't mentioned?

daily routine   family   favourite food   favourite TV programme   job   likes and dislikes

_______________   _______________

Stay-at-home Mum

Fiona Gilbert is married with three teenage sons. Her husband gets up early every morning and goes to work by train. He works in a bank in the centre of London. The boys leave for school at 8am and Fiona puts away the breakfast things and turns on the dishwasher. Fiona goes to work at about nine o'clock, but she doesn't travel very far. Her office is in the spare bedroom in the house. That's because Fiona is one of the 3.7 million people in the UK who work but don't go out to work. They are homeworkers.

Fiona is a freelance writer and a finance expert. Every week she writes articles for magazines and newspapers. She describes how people can save money. Occasionally, she appears on TV too. Fiona really enjoys her job. She says that the best thing about it is when it's warm and sunny. She doesn't stay at her desk. She takes her laptop into the garden and works outside. It isn't all good though. Fiona sends and receives a lot of emails every day, but sometimes she doesn't speak to anyone all day. She hates that.

Fiona turns off her laptop when the boys come back from school. They sit down together and chat about their day at school. Fiona becomes a mother again then, and starts making dinner for her family.

2 Read the article again and complete the summary.

children   home   money   negative   positive   woman

The article is about a British [1] ______________, Fiona Gilbert, who works from [2] ______________. She knows a lot of things about [3] ______________ for her job. Fiona is mostly [4] ______________ about what she does, but she is [5] ______________ about one thing. She stops working in the afternoon to talk to her [6] ______________.

3 Read the article again and answer these questions.

1 What does Mr Gilbert do?
____
2 What does Fiona do before she goes to work?
____
3 How many British people are homeworkers?
____
4 What does Fiona write about in her articles?
____
5 Where does she work when the weather is good?
____
6 How does she usually communicate with people at work?
____
7 Does Fiona cook?
____

4 Complete the phrasal verbs with the prepositions in the box.

WORD ZONE EXTRA

off   away   on   out   up

1 put _ _ _ _ things
2 turn _ _ a machine
3 turn _ _ _ a machine
4 find _ _ _ information
5 look _ _ a word

5 Complete the sentences with the phrasal verbs in exercise 4.

1 We ______________ difficult words in our dictionaries.
2 I never ______________ my phone. It's on all the time.
3 If you go online, you can ______________ about everything.
4 My parents ______________ the radio when they wake up.
5 Do you ______________ your clothes when you go to bed?

VOCABULARY Everyday activities

6 Complete the table with the words in the box.

breakfast to the cinema dinner dressed your homework the housework online ready for bed to school (x2) a shower a snack sport

have	go

get	do

7 Complete the texts with the correct form of the verbs in the box.

brush do have meet tidy visit

Help! My sister is always in the bathroom. She [1] __________ a shower every morning and evening, and she [2] __________ her teeth about six times a day!

My brother doesn't help at home. He never [3] __________ the housework and he [4] __________ his room once every six months. He's lazy!

Weekends are great! I usually [5] __________ friends in town on Saturdays and on Sundays we [6] __________ my grandparents. I love them!

8 Write true sentences for you with the words in brackets. Choose from the verbs in exercises 6 and 7.

1 (I / every morning)

____

2 (my father or mother / after school)

____

3 (me and my friends / at the weekend)

____

WANT TO KNOW MORE?
Everyday activities

9 Match photos 1–8 with verbs A–H. Use a dictionary if you need to.

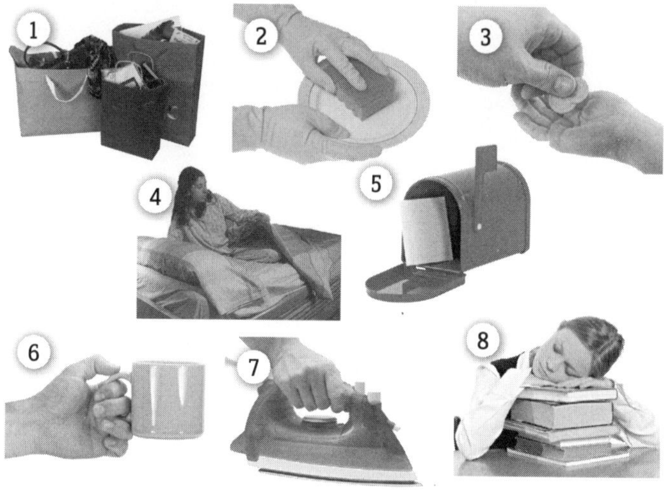

A do the ironing
B go to sleep
C get a letter
D have a drink
E go shopping
F do the washing up
G have a rest
H get pocket money

1__ 2__ 3__ 4__ 5__ 6__ 7__ 8__

10 Complete the sentences with the correct form of the verbs in exercise 9.

1 My parents __________ from the bank once a month.
2 After dinner I __________ for my mum, but I sometimes break a plate!
3 My sister loves clothes and she __________ in town with her friends every Saturday.
4 People often __________ first thing in the morning. It's normally a cup of tea in the UK.
5 Many children __________ from their parents once a week. It's normally about £6.50 a week.
6 I read in bed at night before I __________ .
7 When Ben gets home from school, he __________ on the sofa and then he does his homework.
8 'Do you __________ in your house?' 'Sometimes, but shirts are impossible to do!'

11 How often do you do the activities in exercise 9? Write true sentences for you with these time expressions in brackets.

(everyday) ____________________

(once or twice a week) ____________________

(once or twice a month) ____________________

(never) ____________________

GRAMMAR Adverbs of frequency | *can* / *can't*

1 Complete the diagram with adverbs of frequency.

hardly ever never not often
sometimes usually

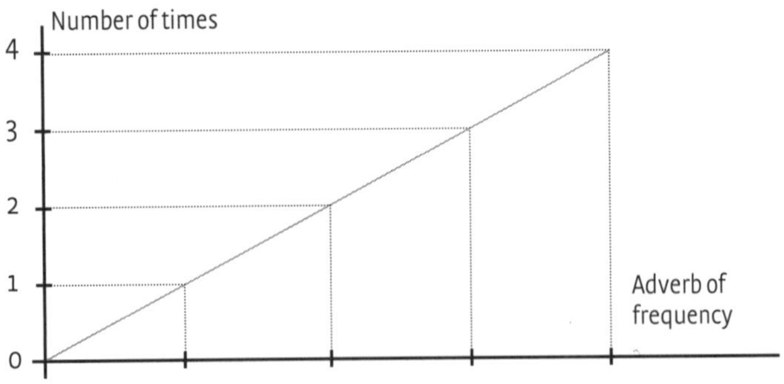

2 Rewrite the sentences using the adverb of frequency in brackets.

1 I get up early on Sunday mornings.
(never) ____________________

2 You are late for school.
(not often) ____________________

3 It is cold in summer.
(rarely) ____________________

4 My mum visits my grandma on Sundays.
(always) ____________________

5 We aren't hungry after school.
(usually) ____________________

6 Ann goes online.
(occasionally) ____________________

7 The children do the housework.
(hardly ever) ____________________

3 Circle the correct words.

My grandpa has got a computer, but he [1] **often / hardly ever** uses it. [2] **Sometimes / Rarely**, he wants to write a letter. He knows where the on button is, so he can [3] **always / not often** turn the computer on, but he can [4] **never / usually** remember how to open a document. So, what does he do? He [5] **not often / usually** phones me and I tell him exactly what to do!

4 Complete the exchanges with *can* or *can't* and the correct verb.

cook eat wait

Max: I'm really hungry. I [1] __________ to eat.
Joe: Here you are.
Max: I'm sorry, but I [2] __________ meat. I'm a vegetarian.
Joe: Well, I [3] __________ an omelette instead.

brush find use

Emma: Mum! I [4] __________ my toothbrush, so I [5] __________ my teeth.
Mum: You [6] __________ the blue toothbrush. It's new.
Emma: OK, thanks!

come do help

Luca: Gina, it's no good. I [7] __________ my maths homework.
Gina: James and I [8] __________ to your house later and we [9] __________ you. We're good at maths.
Luca: Thanks! That'd be great.

5 Write the questions with *can*. Then write true answers for you.

1 you / eat two big pizzas
____________________?

2 your best friend / count in Portuguese
____________________?

3 you and your friends / speak English well
____________________?

4 you / buy stamps in a newsagent's
____________________?

5 your mum / play rugby
____________________?

6 your teacher / cook paella
____________________?

EXTRA CHALLENGE

Choose a famous person you want to interview. Write six questions about their everyday activities and abilities. Use the question words and verbs below to help you. Then invent their answers.

An interview with

____

Robert Pattinson

Adele

Novak Djokovic

cook do sport do the housework eat pizza go on holiday go shopping go to sleep go to the cinema have breakfast play computer games speak (a language) visit relatives wake up watch TV

can how often what what time when where why

Questions	Answers
1 …………	…………
2 …………	…………
3 …………	…………
4 …………	…………
5 …………	…………

WEBQUEST

Go online and find the answers to the questions.

1 What state in the USA is Chicago in?
____

2 What is the name of Chicago's professional basketball team?
____

3 In which Canadian city were the Winter Olympics in 2010?
____

4 Where is the Hôtel de Glace in Canada? What is it?
____

5 Smith is the most common surname in the UK. What is the second most common?
____

6 What are two of the most common surnames in your country?
____

PUZZLE

Look at the code and write the questions. Then write true answers for you.

1	2	3	4	5	6	7	8	9	10	11	12	13	14	15	16	17	18	19	20	21	22	23
L	T	H	A	G	D	M	C	R	U	N	W	O	E	I	K	Y	N	S	P	B	F	V

12 3 14 9 14 | 6 13 14 19 | 17 13 10 9 | 21 14 19 2 | 22 9 15 14 18 6 | 1 15 23 14 ?

______________________ ? ______________

3 13 12 | 13 22 2 14 18 | 6 13 | 17 13 10 | 2 15 6 17 | 17 13 10 9 | 9 13 13 7 ?

______________________ ? ______________

12 3 4 2 | 2 15 7 14 | 6 13 | 17 13 10 | 10 19 10 4 1 1 17 | 3 4 23 14 | 6 15 18 18 14 9 ?

______________________ ? ______________

6 13 | 17 13 10 | 20 9 14 22 14 9 | 21 13 13 16 19 | 13 9 | 8 13 7 20 10 2 14 9 | 5 4 7 14 19 ?

______________________ ? ______________

8 4 18 | 17 13 10 | 19 20 14 4 16 | 8 3 15 18 14 19 14 ?

______________________ ? ______________

1

INTERACTION Meeting new people

1 Answer the questions. Can you remember how to express yourself?

What do you say ...

1 to say "hello" in an informal way?

____

2 to say "hello" at 3pm in a formal way?

____

3 to say "how are you" in an informal way??

____

4 to introduce yourself to someone in a formal way?

____

5 to respond to someone when he / she introduces himself / herself to you in a formal way?

____

6 when you go to bed?

____

2 (3) Complete the exchanges with the correct words. Listen and check.

Jim: [1] ____________ morning. How are you?
Dan: Very well, thanks. How [2] ____________ you?
Jim: I don't feel very well, [3] ____________ .

Kate: Hi, Martin. [4] ____________ you know Alexa?
Martin: No, I don't. Nice to [5] ____________ you.
Alexa: You [6] ____________ .

Tom: [7] ____________ are things, Billy?
Billy: [8] ____________ bad, but my Maths class starts in two minutes.
Tom: OK. [9] ____________ you.
Billy: Yeah, bye.

3 Read the dialogue. Circle T (true) or F (false).

Cara: Hi, Harry. How are you?
Harry: Good, thanks. And you?
Cara: Yeah, I'm fine. Do you know Jenny?
Harry: No, I don't. Do you live in Hale?
Jenny: Yes, I do. What about you?
Harry: I don't live in Hale, but I go to school here.
Jenny: Do you go to Dean Boys' School?
Harry: Yeah, I'm in Year 9.
Jenny: My friend Max Clifton is in that year. Do you know him?
Harry: He's in my class. He usually sits next to me in science and Maths.
Jenny: Really? He's a good friend. We often go the cinema at weekends. Let's go together next time.
Harry: Cool. See you soon. Bye.

1 Cara isn't very well. T / F
2 Harry and Jenny know each other. T / F
3 They live in the same town. T / F
4 Harry is at the same school as Max. T / F
5 Jenny doesn't know Max well. T / F
6 Jenny and Harry plan to meet up with Max. T / F

4 Complete the dialogue with Harry.

Harry: Hello. My name's Harry.
You: (Greet Harry and introduce yourself.)
1 ______________________
Harry: It's nice to meet you.
You: (Agree with Harry.)
2 ______________________
Harry: How are things?
You: (Tell him you're fine. Then ask about him.)
3 ______________________
Harry: Very well, thanks. What's your phone number?
You: (Say your mobile number.)
4 ______________________
Harry: Great. Let's meet on Saturday. See you.
You: (Say goodbye to Harry.)
5 ______________________

YOUR TURN TO SPEAK

5 (4) Revise the *Express yourself* box on page 16 of the Student's Book. Then listen to the people and respond.

WRITING A personal description

WRITING SKILL Using conjunctions

1 Match 1–6 with A–F to make sentences.

1 We play football
2 It isn't close to any towns
3 I've got a lot of e-friends,
4 I live in Birdsville with my parents
5 it hasn't got a cinema
6 They live near the beach,

A or cities.
B so we often go surfing.
C or a shopping mall.
D but I'd love to have more.
E and table tennis.
F and my brother, Riley.

1 __ 2 __ 3 __ 4 __ 5 __ 6 __

2 Complete the text with the sentences in exercise 1.

Hi there!

I'm Cooper. I'm 12 years old and I'm from Australia.
1 ______________________ .
Birdsville is a small town in the Outback.
2 ______________________ .
It's got a population of about 150, but thousands of people visit every year in September for the Birdsville Races.

Birdsville has got some shops and a hotel in the centre of town, but 3 ______________________ .
It's also got a sports centre, so I sometimes meet my friends there. 4 ______________________ .
My grandparents live in Brisbane, Australia's third city. We occasionally visit them and I love it.
5 ______________________ .

Life in Birdsville can be boring, so I always go online in my free time. 6 ______________________ .
Please write and tell me about you!

3 Read the text again and answer the questions.

1 Is Cooper an only child?
____
2 How many people live in Birdsville?
____
3 When are the Birdsville Races?
____
4 Can Cooper go to the cinema in his town?
____
5 Does he enjoy visiting his grandparents? Why?
____
6 How does he spend his free time at home?
____
7 Has Cooper got any online friends?
____

4 Look at the *Writing Reference* on page 113. Then write a reply to Cooper's message. Invent a different identity. Write about your:

- personal details
- family
- home town
- free time

Reminder
- Use the present simple.
- Check 3rd person singular forms.
- Use *and, but, or, so.*
- Use adverbs of frequency.

____
____
____
____
____
____
____
____
____
____
____
____
____
____
____
____
____
____
____
____

2 Get active

READING

1 Read the text quickly. What type of text is it?

Are you doing anything interesting this Easter?
Why don't you try parkour at Longton Park?
It's fun, safe, energetic and FREE!
For beginners and people with some experience.

1st Week course:	10 – 14 years
Tuesday & Wednesday	10 am – 2 am
2nd Week course:	15 years +
Thursday & Friday	10 am – 2 am

Parkour, or PK, is an exciting activity that is becoming popular with young people around the world today. It's a form of movement you use to get from one object to another as quickly as possible. Parkour started in France and its name comes from the French word for assault course – *parcours du combattant*. A bit like gymnastics, you run, jump, twist and turn when you do PK, but you aren't in a gym. You're in a town or city and the permanent objects in the urban landscape such as walls or fences are your assault course.

Parkour isn't easy, but it's a challenge and a good way to keep fit. Most people who do the sport are males from 14–24 years old, but more and more girls are starting to do it regularly. So, what are you waiting for? You don't need any special equipment, just wear trainers and comfortable clothes.

Phone 020 4098 51 and book your place on a course today! It'll be brilliant!

2 Read the text again and answer the questions. Circle *A*, *B* or *C*.

1 What is the aim of the text?
A To tell people about Outward Bound courses.
B To tell people about an unusual sport called parkour which you can do at Longton Park.
C To tell people about gymnastics around the world.

2 Why are there two courses?
A They're for people of different abilities.
B They're for people of different ages.
C They're at different times of the day.

3 What are the origins of parkour?
A It originated in France and is now a global activity.
B It started in Longton Park and then moved to France.
C It originated in France and only the French do it.

4 What do you actually do in parkour?
A You do an assault course in a gym.
B You build objects in a town or city.
C You use objects in a town or city as an assault course.

5 How would you define PK?
A An activity that men of all ages and young women do.
B An activity that only young men do.
C An activity that male and female teenagers and young adults do.

WORD ZONE EXTRA

Opinion adjectives

3 Look at the opinion adjectives. Find their opposites in the text.

1 boring ≠ ______
2 dangerous ≠ ______
3 temporary ≠ ______
4 difficult ≠ ______
5 awful ≠ ______

VOCABULARY Sports

4 Write the sports.

On ice or snow	On wheels
1 i__ h_____	3 s____b___d___
2 s__i__	4 m___t___ b_____

On or in water	On a court
5 s___m___	9 t__n__
6 k___k___	10 v____y____
7 s__l___	11 b____t____
8 s__f___	

5 Complete the advert with *play*, *go* or *do*.

Be active at Manor Farm!

There are fantastic outdoor facilities at Manor Farm for you to [1] ________ athletics or to [2] ________ rugby. You can even [3] ________ horse riding there!
If you prefer being inside, you can [4] ________ five-a-side football in the sports hall or [5] ________ gymnastics in the gym. Also learn to [6] ________ baseball this summer with an American coach!

6 Write sentences with the words in brackets. Use the words in the box and the correct form of *play*, *go* or *do*.

at weekends   every week   never   sometimes

1 (I / mountain biking)
____

2 (my best friend / gymnastics)
____

3 (my parents / tennis)
____

4 (my brother / volleyball)
____

5 (I / swimming)
____

WANT TO KNOW MORE? Sports

7 Complete the diagram with the words in the box. Use a dictionary if you need to.

~~aerobics~~ ~~badminton~~ ~~cycling~~ jogging a marathon snowboarding squash table tennis a triathlon

DO	PLAY	GO
aerobics	*badminton*	*cycling*
________	________	________
________	________	________

8 Do the quiz about the sports in exercise 7.

1. Physical exercises that you do to music.
2. An event where you swim, cycle and run.
3. Ping-pong is an informal word for this.
4. Two players play this on a court with a ball.
5. An event where you run 42.195 kilometres.
6. A form of exercise where you run slowly.
7. A form of exercise where you ride a bike.

9 Choose four sports in exercise 7. Write what you think about them.

1 *I think squash is fun, but very tiring.*
2 ____________________
3 ____________________
4 ____________________
5 ____________________

2

GRAMMAR Present continuous

1 Look at the photo. Complete the text with the correct form of the verbs.

do hope jump lose play run try (x2)

REDS 59 WHITES 27

1 ________ these sportspeople ________ athletics? No, they aren't. They 2 ________ basketball.
At the moment, it's 59-27 to the Reds, so the Whites 3 ________ the match. The player with the ball is called Jackson. He 4 ________ fast and he 5 ________ high because he 6 ________ to score. The players on the other team 7 ________ to stop him, but they 8 ________ that Jackson misses the basket!

2 What are people at the match saying? Write their comments.

1 we / have a great time
____
2 I / get / a drink
____
3 my team / not win
____
4 everyone / shout
____
5 they / not play well
____
6 we / share / some popcorn
____

3 Write questions using the present continuous about the photo in exercise 1.

1 the match / take place / inside
________?
2 the spectators / stand / on the court
________?
3 the players / wear / trainers
________?
4 Jackson / sit down
________?
5 Jackson / play / well
________?

4 Complete the phone conversations with the correct form of the verbs in brackets.

Nia: Hello. Is Hayley there?
Bill: No, she isn't. She 1 ________ (hike) with friends in Wales at the moment.
Nia: Really? 2 ________ (they / camp)?
Bill: No, they aren't. They 3 ________ (stay) in a youth hostel.

Gina: Dad, it's Gina. What 4 ________ (you / do) at home today? It's Friday.
Dad: I've got the day off, so I 5 ________ (not work). I 6 ________ (sit) on the sofa with your mum at the moment. We 7 ________ (watch) a good film.
Gina: That's great!

Jake: Hi. Can I speak to Ruth, please?
Inés: Not at the moment. She 8 ________ (drive).
Jake: Tell her that I 9 ________ (not wait) for her outside the cinema. We are in the cafeteria next door.
Inés: OK. We 10 ________ (arrive) at the car park right now.

5 What are you doing at the moment? Write two affirmative and two negative sentences.

1 ________
2 ________
3 ________
4 ________

LISTENING

1 Write the words under the correct heading in the table. Use a dictionary if you need to.

1 climbing climb climber

2 competitor competition compete

3 break a record record-breaking record-breaker

	verb	noun (person)	noun (thing)	adjective
1	*climb*			✗
2				✗
3			✗	

2 5 Listen to a conversation. Where's Ben? Is he outside or inside?

3 5 Listen again and complete the summary with the correct information.

Ben is telling his mum about a sport called 1 ____________ .

There are 2 ____________ people in each race. The first person to get to 3 ____________ of the wall is the winner.

Ben thinks this sport is really 4 ____________ because of the speed. The record-breaking time for a 15-metre climb is 5 ____________ seconds.

The climbers use 6 ____________ for safety. Competitors must be 7 ____________ ____________ and strong.

TEST YOUR MEMORY!

4 Circle T (true) or F (false). Then correct the false sentences.

1 Ben is in an old church. T / F
2 The 15-metre world record holder is from the UK. T / F
3 Ben thinks the sport is safe. T / F
4 It's impossible to fall to the ground. T / F
5 Ben isn't competing in the competition. T / F
6 Ben's mum is watching him. T / F

____
____
____

5 Write these sentences in your language.

1 It's a type of sports centre now.
____
2 I see. Is it exciting?
____
3 What a record-breaker!
____
4 I love a challenge.
____

READING

1 Read the text quickly. Is Claudia positive or negative about BMX racing?

The 60 second interview with ...

I'm at a BMX track near Manchester with 13-year-old BMX rider Claudia Read. Claudia is having a break from her practice session, so let's chat to her now. She doesn't keep still for long!

1 ____________________

BMX means Bicycle Motocross. It's a type of racing on a bike, but you don't do it on roads. You do it on special race tracks where there are jumps. Look at that guy over there! He's standing up on his bike now and jumping. It's awesome.

2 ____________________

Everyone in my family is sports mad. My brothers play footie all the time. I love doing athletics. I can run 100 metres in thirteen seconds, but I prefer doing BMX.

3 ____________________

I fall off occasionally, but normally I don't hurt myself badly. BMX riders always wear special gear for protection, like elbow and knee pads. A helmet is really important too. I've got two but this red one I'm wearing now is my favourite. I usually win my races when I wear it!

4 ____________________

It isn't difficult to ride a BMX bike. They're a bit like kids' bikes, but you need strength and courage to take part in a race and win. You can't do it if you're a wimp! I've got four brothers and I'm the youngest in the family, so I guess I'm quite tough. I'm competitive, too. I hate losing!

5 ____________________

BMX racing is an Olympic sport now, so my ambition is to compete in the Olympic Games and be on telly. I often dream about winning. In my dream, I'm standing on top of the podium and someone is putting a gold medal around my neck. It's an awesome feeling!

Well, good luck, Claudia. I hope your dream comes true.

2 Complete the text with the questions below. There is one question you do not need.

Are you very sporty?
How often do you have accidents?
What do you hope to do in the future?
What exactly is BMX racing?
What gear are you wearing now?
Why are you good at BMX racing?

3 Read the text again and answer the questions.

1 Is Claudia very active? What part of the introduction tells you?
____
2 Where do people ride BMX bikes?
____
3 What does Claudia's family all love doing?
____
4 Why does Claudia love her red helmet?
____
5 What qualities does she think are important for BMX racing?
____
6 How many children are there in her family?
____
7 Where is Claudia in her dream?
____

EXTRA WORD ZONE

Informal expressions

4 Find informal words in the text for the words below.

1 man ____________________
2 football ____________________
3 children ____________________
4 coward ____________________
5 TV ____________________

5 Complete the text with the informal words in exercise 4.

We're watching a ¹ ____________________ match on the ² ____________________ at the moment.

It's Manchester United against Arsenal and it's really exciting. I want United to win. Go on, Rooney! Don't be a ³ ____________________! Get the ball from that Arsenal player!

Wait a minute! What's happening? There's a ⁴ ____________________ on the pitch. It's an Arsenal fan.

VOCABULARY Sports venues & equipment

6 Match 1–7 with A–G to make sports venues.

1 tennis	A slope
2 swimming	B rink
3 skate	C court
4 football	D track
5 ski	E pitch
6 ice	F pool
7 running	G park

1_ 2_ 3_ 4_ 5_ 6_ 7_

7 Do the sports equipment quiz.

1 You wear this on your head when you go cycling. __________

2 You stand on this when you go surfing. __________

3 You hit the ball with this when you play tennis. __________

4 You score a basket through this when you play basketball. __________

5 You wear these on your feet when you are on ice. __________

6 You hit the ball with this when you play baseball. __________

8 Write present continuous sentences. What sport is he playing?

1 (he / wear / knee and elbow pads)
____

2 (he / hold / a stick)
____

3 (he / stand / on an ice rink)
____

He is playing __________

WANT TO KNOW MORE? Sports equipment

9 Complete the sentences with the words in the box. Use a dictionary if you need to.

face guard gloves goggles inline skates life jacket swimming cap wetsuit

Whee Chye is playing canoe polo. He's wearing a helmet with a [1] __________. He's got number ten on his [2] __________.

Donna loves wild swimming. She's wearing a black [3] __________. She's also wearing a pink [4] __________ on her hair and a pair of [5] __________ over her eyes.

Kyle and Tom are playing inline hockey. They're wearing [6] __________ on their feet. They're also wearing [7] __________ on their hands. Kyle and Tom are really good at hockey.

10 Complete the sentences with the sports equipment in exercise 9.

1 You must always wear a __________ when you go sailing.
2 I can see underwater because I wear __________.
3 There are eight wheels on a pair of __________.
4 Surfers in the UK often wear a __________ to keep warm.
5 Meg is the goalkeeper on our hockey team, so she wears a __________ to protect her face.
6 If you've got long hair, it isn't easy to put on a __________.
7 Is it difficult to hold a hockey stick when you're wearing thick __________?

11 Do you or your friends wear the sports equipment in exercise 9 to play your favourite sports? Write three true sentences.

1 __________
2 __________
3 __________

GRAMMAR Present continuous & present simple | State verbs

1 Write sentences using the present simple or present continuous of the verbs.

1 a fan / run / on the pitch / at the moment
____

2 you / prefer / BMX bikes / or / mountain bikes
______________________________?

3 how often / you / practise
______________________________?

4 I / not think / badminton / be / very interesting
____

5 she / never / watch / sport on TV
____

2 Write the sentences from exercise 1 under the correct heading.

activities in progress / temporary situations
____
____

routines / facts
____
____

opinions / thoughts / feelings
____
____

3 Complete the text with the present simple or present continuous of the verbs in brackets.

Here I am at the London Marathon. It's one of the biggest running events in the world and it [1] ____________ (take) place every year at the end of April. As you know, I usually [2] ____________ (do) the marathon, but I [3] ____________ (not do) it this year because of a problem with my knee. My colleague, Dan Elliot, [4] ____________ (run) the race for the first time today. It's difficult to see people amongst the runners, but I [5] ____________ (not think) it'll be difficult to see Dan this year. He [6] ____________ (not wear) the usual running gear. He's a giant banana! Dan [7] ____________ (say) that it isn't easy running in fancy dress, but he's determined to finish the race. He [8] ____________ (want) to raise £10,000 for a children's charity. Good luck, Dan!

4 Write questions using the present simple or present continuous with the words below.

1 have got / you / an e-reader
______________________________?

2 how often / you / listen / to music
______________________________?

3 what / you / do / before / you / go / to sleep
______________________________?

4 what / you / read / at the moment
______________________________?

5 what / you / think / of e-readers
______________________________?

6 you / know / Justin Bieber
______________________________?

7 you / study / for exams / right now
______________________________?

5 Complete the interview with the questions in exercise 4.

Meet Jenni Layton. She's a young runner who is training to do the London Marathon.

Tom: [1] ______________________________?
Jenni: Most of the time, I play a lot of music at home and I always listen to music on my MP3 player when I'm running. It helps me concentrate.
Tom: [2] ______________________________?
Jenni: Of course I do! I love his music. I've got all his songs on my MP3 player.
Tom: [3] ______________________________?
Jenni: I find it difficult to fall asleep, so I always read in bed for about half an hour.
Tom: [4] ______________________________?
Jenni: The Hunger Games by Suzanne Collins, it's science fiction and it's really entertaining!
Tom: [5] ______________________________?
Jenni: Yes, I have. I got one for Christmas last year.
Tom: [6] ______________________________?
Jenni: They're awesome. It's amazing to have thousands of books on one small device. I never buy paper books anymore.
Tom: [7] ______________________________?
Jenni: No, not really. They start in June so I can concentrate on my running until the end of April.

6 Now write true answers for you to three of the questions in exercise 4.

1 **Question** ___ : ______________________________
2 **Question** ___ : ______________________________
3 **Question** ___ : ______________________________

EXTRA CHALLENGE

There are seven mistakes in the description of the picture. Rewrite it correctly.

On the left, there is a boy riding a BMX bike. He's doing a trick. On the right, there are two girls doing gymnastics. They are standing on the ground. One of them is trying to score a goal and the other is trying to stop her. Three people are sitting in the middle of the picture. They are having an argument. In the foreground, there are lots of tall buildings. It's a large city.

____

____

____

____

____

____

____

____

____

WEBQUEST

Go online and find the answers to the questions.

1 In what town in England is the head office of the Outward Bound Trust?
____

2 How much is an Outward Bound Men's T-shirt in the online shop?
____

3 What is the length of an ice hockey match?
____

4 How many players are there on the rink during an ice hockey match?
____

5 How many times a year do the X Games take place? In which country?
____

6 What type of sports can you see at the X Games?
____

PUZZLE

Copy the words with the same symbols. Put them in order to make questions. Then write true answers for you.

WHO ♦	ARE ⊙	HOW ★	YOU ⊙
DO ★	YOUR ♦	GO ★	SPORTSPERSON ♦
WHAT ⊙	OFTEN ★	NOW ⊙	FAVOURITE ♦
CYCLING ★	IS ♦	DOING ⊙	YOU ★

♦ Question: ______________________________?
Answer: ______________________________

★ Question: ______________________________?
Answer: ______________________________

⊙ Question: ______________________________?
Answer: ______________________________

INTERACTION On the phone

1 Answer the questions. Can you remember how to express yourself?

What do you say ...

1 if you're a receptionist and you answer the phone?

____

2 to ask about closing times?

____

3 to ask about ticket prices?

____

4 when you want to speak to Tom?

____

5 to find out who is on the phone?

____

2 (6) Circle the correct words. Listen and check.

Receptionist: Hello. 1 **Who / How / What** can I help you?
Caller: 2 **I / I'm / I'd** like to ask about gym membership.
Receptionist: You need to speak to the manager, but she isn't 3 **where / here / there** at the moment.

Will: Can I 4 **tell / leave / speak** to Callum, please?
Mrs Crane: Certainly. 5 **Who's / How's / Whose** calling?
Will: It's Will 6 **chatting / saying / speaking**.

3 Read the dialogues and answer the questions.

1 Where does Mark work?

____

2 What does Jamie want to know?

____

3 Can he speak to Ed? Why?

____

4 What does Jamie do then?

____

5 What's the problem with their arrangement?

____

Mark: The Football Centre. Mark speaking.
Jamie: Hi, there. I'd like to ask for some information.
Mark: That's fine. How can I help you?
Jamie: What time do you open on Sundays?
Mark: We're only open from Monday to Saturday from midday till 8pm.
Jamie: Really?
Mark: Yes, we're closed on Sundays.
Jamie: OK. Thanks for your help.

Mr Jones: Hello.
Jamie: Hi. Can I speak to Ed, please?
Mr Jones: I'm sorry, but Ed isn't here at the moment. Who's calling?
Jamie: It's Jamie. I'm a friend from school.
Mr Jones: Hello, Jamie. It's Mr Jones here.
Jamie: Hi, Mr Jones. Can I leave a message, please?
Mr Jones: Sure. No problem.
Jamie: Can you tell him that we can't play footie on Sunday. The Football Centre isn't open, but how about playing on Monday evening instead?
Mr Jones: OK. I'll give him the message when I see him.
Jamie: Thanks. Bye.

4 Complete the dialogue with a caller.

You: (Answer the phone and say who you are.)
1 ______________________________
Mary: Hi. Can I speak to Leah, please?
You: (Say that she isn't there. Ask who it is.)
2 ______________________________
Mary: It's Mary.
You: (Offer to take a message.)
3 ______________________________
Mary: Yes, please. Can you tell her to meet me outside the ice rink at 4.30.
You: (Check the message.)
4 ______________________________
Mary: That's right.
You: (Ask her about ticket prices.)
5 ______________________________
Mary: It's €8.00 including the skates.
You: (Thank Mary and say goodbye.)
6 ______________________________

YOUR TURN TO SPEAK

5 (7) Revise the *Express yourself* box on page 26 of the Student's Book. Then listen to the people and respond.

WRITING A description of a sport

WRITING SKILL Using punctuation

1 Rewrite the sentences with the correct punctuation.

1 to do horse boarding you need a horse an off-road board and a horse rider

____

2 hes organizing a horse boarding championship in july

____

3 horse boarding is daniels idea and hes the founder of the extreme horse riding association

____

4 its a combination of horse riding skateboarding and mountain boarding

____

5 its easy to fall off when youre horse boarding so special clothing is very important

____

2 Complete the text with the sentences in exercise 1.

Horse boarding

Extreme sports are all about excitement and danger, and new ones are invented every year. They're often a combination of two or more sports that already exist. One of the latest ones in the UK is horse boarding. [1] _______________ [2] _______________ You also need an off-road board, the kind that mountain boarders use, and a rope. The idea is that the horse and rider pull the board rider as fast as possible. Reaching speeds of up to 56 kph, this isn't a sport for wimps.

[3] _______________
Board riders wear protective suits, helmets, goggles, and pads. Other than that, a board rider needs balance and a lot of courage.

Daniel Fowler-Prime is a professional stunt horse rider. Two of the films he's in are The Da Vinci Code and Kingdom of Heaven. [4] _______________ He's also got a training ground near Wolverhampton in England.

Horse boarding is becoming popular with people around the country, and Daniel is busy with the sport.
[5] _______________
Another of Daniel's extreme sports is horse surfing. What will he think of next?

3 Read the text again and tick (✓) YES or NO.

		YES	NO
1	Horse boarding isn't a new sport.	☐	☐
2	Horse boarders use a lot of equipment.	☐	☐
3	Daniel Fowler-Prime rides horses in his job.	☐	☐
4	More people are doing horse boarding.	☐	☐
5	There aren't any horse boarding competitions at the moment.	☐	☐

4 Look at the *Writing Reference* on page 114. Then write an article about an unusual sport. Invent the name of the sport and the details. Write about:

- the number of players
- equipment
- length of game
- rules
- your opinion of the sport

Reminder

- Use a capital letter at the beginning and a full stop at the end of a sentence.
- Also use capital letters for names, places, days of the week and months.
- Use an apostrophe in contractions, and to show possession.
- Use a comma to separate two parts of a sentence and in a list.

____

3 Food for thought

READING

1 Read the texts. What are they?

A adverts B reviews C special offers D menus

2 Match the comments in the box with the correct restaurant.

Needs tables and chairs. Good value for money. Extremely slow!

Amber

Emma
Manchester, UK

"________________________________"

The food at Amber can sometimes be expensive, but they do a special set menu from Sunday to Friday between 6pm and 10pm. There's a choice of five starters, five main courses and five desserts on it, and they change it every month. You can choose two courses for £12.50 or three for £16.50, so it's reasonable. There's a chocolate brownie dessert on the menu at the moment and it's delicious!

Jojo's

Martin
Bury, UK

"________________________________"

Jojo's has got a new manager and the service is awful now. When you sit down at your table, it takes 20 minutes just to get the menu. Then you can wait an hour and a half before the waiter serves your food. When you get the bill at the end of the meal, the waiter expects a tip. What a cheek! I'm looking for a new place to eat now.

Burger Bar

Tilly
Stockport, UK

"________________________________"

Think of burgers and you usually think of fast food restaurants, but Burger Bar is different. The burgers are handmade from good quality beef and they're delicious! You can also choose some unusual toppings for your burger. My brother's favourite is coleslaw and grapes. Weird! The only problem with this place is that it's a takeaway. I prefer eating my burger in a restaurant.

3 Read the texts again and circle T (true) or F (false).

1 You can have the set menu at Amber any time. T / F
2 There are fifteen things on the set menu. T / F
3 A starter and a main course cost £16.50. T / F
4 The manager at Jojo's is different from before. T / F
5 The waiter gives you a menu when you arrive at Jojo's. T / F
6 Jojo's is still Martin's favourite restaurant. T / F
7 Tilly thinks the burgers in Burger Bar taste good. T / F
8 She loves the same burger as her brother. T / F
9 You can't eat your food in the Burger Bar. T / F

WORD ZONE EXTRA

At a restaurant

4 Look at the definitions. Find the correct words in the text.

1 ________________________: A menu that has a fixed price and a limited number of dishes on it.
2 ________________________: A piece of paper that tells you how much to pay for your food / drinks in a restaurant.
3 ________________________: The extra money you give a waiter in a restaurant for good service.
4 ________________________: Not made by a machine.
5 ________________________: Things that you put on top of food.

5 Write true answers to these questions.

1 What food do you think is delicious?

____

2 Who normally pays the bill when you go to a restaurant?

____

3 What are your favourite toppings on a pizza?

____

VOCABULARY Food

6 Write the headings in the correct place. Then complete the words with the correct vowels.

carbohydrates dairy products
fish fruit meat vegetables

1 ______________ s _ lm _ n t _ n _	4 ______________ gr _ p _ s p _ _ ch str _ wb _ rr _ _ s p _ n _ _ ppl _
2 ______________ p _ st _ r _ c _ br _ _ d fl _ _ r	5 ______________ m _ lk y _ gh _ rt b _ tt _ r ch _ _ s _
3 ______________ p _ rk b _ _ f ch _ ck _ n	6 ______________ p _ _ s c _ bb _ g _ l _ tt _ c _ gr _ _ n b _ _ ns

7 Complete the sentences with the words in the box.

cucumbers oil onions
peppers prawns tomatoes

1 ______________ can be green, yellow or red.
2 ______________ are grey when they're raw and pink when they're cooked.
3 There are different types of ______________, such as olive, sunflower and vegetable.
4 ______________ are normally green on the outside, but they're white inside.
5 ______________ are normally yellow or red, but some are white too.
6 ______________ are green, and then they become red.

8 Write full sentences that are true for you.

1 A vegetable that you love and one that you hate
____
2 A fruit that you never eat
____
3 A dairy product you have every day
____

WANT TO KNOW MORE?
Food

9 Label the recipes. Use two of the names in the box. Use a dictionary if you need to.

carrot soup spaghetti bolognese
chocolate brownies chilli con carne

1 ______________	2 ______________
• 250 g butter • 200 g dark chocolate • 50 g chopped nuts (optional) • 80 g cocoa powder • 65 g flour • 360 g sugar • 4 large eggs • zest of 1 orange (optional)	• 1 teaspoon vegetable oil • 1 onion • 1 potato • 450 g carrots • 1.2l vegetable stock • salt • pepper

10 Read the definitions. Find the correct words in the recipes in exercise 9.

1 This is sweet. Some people have it in their tea or coffee.
____
2 Orange vegetables.
____
3 We use these two things to season our food.
____
4 A round fruit often used for its juice.
____
5 The fruit of some plants. They are small and hard.
____
6 They come from chickens. People are sometimes allergic to them.
____
7 A liquid made from water and vegetables or meat.
____
8 A round vegetable used to make chips.
____

11 Write true sentences about your preferences for the recipes in exercise 9.

____
____
____
____
____

GRAMMAR Countable & uncountable nouns | *some* / *any* / *no*

1 Circle *C* (countable) and *U* (uncountable), then write the plural of the countable nouns.

1 strawberry C / U ______
2 tomato C / U ______
3 water C / U ______
4 lettuce C / U ______
5 butter C / U ______
6 money C / U ______
7 peach C / U ______
8 potato C / U ______
9 lemon C / U ______
10 rice C / U ______
11 homework C / U ______

2 Circle the correct words.

There's always [1] **a plate / an plate / plate** of fruit on the table in our kitchen. That's because my mum believes that '[2] **a apple / an apple / apple** a day keeps the doctor away'. That's [3] **a expression / an expression / expression** that means that eating [4] **a fruit / fruit / fruits** is healthy for you. Today, there's [5] **a pineapple / an pineapple / pineapples**, three [6] **an apple / apple / apples** and [7] **a bunch of bananas / an bunch of bananas / bunch of bananas** on the plate, but I don't like any of them. My favourite food is [8] **a cheese / cheese / cheeses**. I love all types of it, and I always have it with [9] **a bread / bread / breads**. Cheese is [10] **a dairy product / dairy product / dairy products** like [11] **a milk / milk / milks**, so it contains calcium which is good for you. However, it also contains fat which isn't good for you! My mum wants me to eat less cheese and more [12] **a vegetable / vegetable / vegetables**.

3 Complete the conversations with *some*, *any*, *no* or *a*.

Waiter: What would you like to drink?
Ted: I'd like [1] ______ apple juice, please.
Waiter: Sorry, but there's [2] ______ apple juice today.
Ted: Is there [3] ______ orange juice?
Waiter: Yes, there is, and there's [4] ______ pineapple juice, too.
Ted: I'll have [5] ______ glass of pineapple juice, please.

Ana: Are there [6] ______ vegetarian meals on the menu?
Waiter: Yes, there are. There's [7] ______ vegetarian tart and there are [8] ______ vegetarian starters, too.
Ana: Are there [9] ______ nuts in the vegetarian tart?
Waiter: No, there are [10] ______ nuts in it.
Ana: That's good because I'm allergic to nuts! I'll have that, please.

4 Write sentences about the photo in exercise 2. Use the correct form of *be* and *some*, *any* or *no*.

1 there / be / fruit
______
2 there / not be / strawberries
______
3 there / be / apples
______
4 there / be / grapes
______
5 there / not be / bread
______
6 be / there / bananas?
______

5 What is there in your fridge? Write true sentences about the food in brackets.

1 (butter)
______
2 (eggs)
______
3 (carrots)
______
4 (fish)
______

LISTENING

1 Complete the definitions with the words in the box. Use a dictionary if you need to.

bake bakery grate grater mix
mixer recipe recipe book

1 ____________________, *vb.* To combine two or more things together.

2 ____________________, *vb.* To cut food into small pieces with a special kitchen utensil.

3 ____________________, *n.* The instructions for cooking something.

4 ____________________, *vb.* To cook in an oven: ~ a cake; ~ bread.

5 ____________________, *n.* A kitchen utensil that we use to cut food into small pieces, such as cheese.

6 ____________________, *n.* A shop where they sell cakes, bread, etc.

7 ____________________, *n.* A book that contains the instructions for cooking different dishes.

8 ____________________, *n.* A machine that we use to mix something: a food ~; an electric ~.

2 🎧 8 Listen to a conversation. What exactly is Eva making?

3 🎧 8 Listen again and tick (✓) YES or NO.

		YES	NO
1	There are lots of recipe books in Eva's kitchen.	☐	☐
2	Eva's mum knows what Eva is doing.	☐	☐
3	There's no butter in the recipe.	☐	☐
4	Flour is one of the other ingredients.	☐	☐
5	Eva changes the recipe and adds nuts.	☐	☐
6	Charlie thinks the cake looks disgusting.	☐	☐
7	Eva and Charlie bake the cake for thirty minutes.	☐	☐
8	Eva and Charlie eat some of it.	☐	☐

TEST YOUR MEMORY!

4 Answer the questions.

1 Where is the recipe that Eva is using?

____

2 What is special about the day?

____

3 How old is her mum?

____

4 How many carrots are there in the recipe?

____

5 Who grates the carrots?

____

6 What do they do when the cake is baking?

____

5 Write these sentences in your language.

1 Hang on! Are there carrots in it?

____

2 That's right. There are two eggs in it.

____

3 It's awesome, and it smells delicious.

____

READING

1 Read the webpage quickly. How many countries and nationalities can you find?

Eat your way around the world

Imagine that you're going out for a meal with your family, but you can't agree on a restaurant. Your dad wants to eat Indian food, your mum loves Chinese, your brother only eats pizza, and you'd like to try sushi from Japan. Where can you go to make everyone happy? The answer is The International Buffet.

The International Buffet is a new type of restaurant that doesn't serve food from just one country. There are over 300 dishes from around the world on the menu. There are curries from India and noodle dishes from China. There are Turkish mezzes and Moroccan tagines. There's typical cuisine from Greece and Portugal and there are Mexican tortillas. The list of countries goes on.

All the food is freshly made in The International Buffet by over 40 professional chefs. Most of the cooking takes place in the restaurant's large kitchen, but chefs prepare some dishes at special 'bars' in the restaurant itself. For example, there's a Japanese teppanyaki bar and an Italian pasta bar. For dessert, there's a Belgian waffle bar and an American pancake bar. Diners stand and watch as the chefs cook for them.

The International Buffet is a food lover's paradise. There's space for 600 diners at one time, and it's just £6.99 for lunch and £12.99 for dinner. Kids under 12 are half price. What are you waiting for? Come and travel the world at The International Buffet!

2 Read the webpage again and circle the correct answers.

1 The International Buffet is a good place for people with different ... .
A opinions B food preferences
C nationalities D ages

2 The International Buffet serves food from ... countries.
A 10 B 40
C 300 D many

3 You can watch some chefs cooking ... .
A on TV B in the kitchen
C in the dining room D in other countries

4 One of the ... is pancakes.
A starters B main courses
C desserts D free dishes

5 ... people can eat at The International Buffet at the same time.
A A few B Not many
C Some D A lot of

6 It's cheaper for ... to eat at the restaurant.
A elderly people B the chefs
C young children D young adults

WORD ZONE EXTRA

Countries and nationalities

3 Complete the table with words from the text.

Country	Nationality
Turkey	1
Morocco	2
3	Greek
4	Portuguese
Belgium	5
the USA	6

4 Complete the sentences with some of the countries and nationalities in exercise 3.

1 ____________ is a country in North Africa.
2 New York City is the largest ____________ city.
3 ____________ is a small country between France, Germany and Holland.
4 ____________ yoghurt is one of the best yoghurts in the world.

VOCABULARY At the table | Containers and portions

5 Complete the sentences with the words in the box.

bowl chopsticks cup fork glass
knife napkin plate saucer spoon

1 A typical British breakfast is a ______ of cereal and a ______ of orange juice.

2 In the UK, you use the ______ in your left hand. You cut the food with the ______ in your right hand.

3 To eat soup, you use a soup ______ . It's rude to slurp the soup from it!

4 The traditional way to drink tea in the UK is with a ______ and ______ .

5 When you lay the table, you normally put a paper ______ on everyone's ______ .

6 In Chinese restaurants, you can eat with ______ .

6 Circle the correct words.

1 a **slice / bag / bottle** of olive oil
2 a **jar / piece / slice** of mayonnaise
3 a **carton / packet / bag** of orange juice
4 a **bottle / bag / jar** of bananas
5 a **piece / carton / packet** of biscuits
6 a **slice / bottle / bag** of bread
7 a **carton / can / packet** of tuna
8 a **can / jar / piece** of chocolate cake

7 Imagine you're at the supermarket. Describe four things that you want to buy for lunch. Include the containers.

______
______
______
______
______
______
______
______
______
______

WANT TO KNOW MORE? Containers

8 Match the words in the box with the pictures and use them to complete the shopping list. Use a dictionary if you need to.

cereal chocolate grapes
toilet paper toothpaste yoghurt

A

______

B

______

C

______

D

______

E

______

F

______

1 a box of ______
2 a roll of ______
3 a pot of ______
4 a bunch of ______
5 a tube of ______
6 a bar of ______

9 Complete the exchanges with some of the words in exercise 8.

Lois: Mum! Help! I'm on the toilet and there's no [1] ______ .
Mum: It's OK. There's a new [2] ______ behind you!

Kyle: Mum, I'm at the fruit shop. You've got red [3] ______ on your list, but there are only green ones.
Mum: That's OK. Get a big [4] ______ of green ones instead.

Mum: I want to brush my teeth, but the [5] ______ is dry.
Alex: Why's that?
Mum: Because you never put the lid on the [6] ______ !

Julia: I know that [7] ______ has got a lot of calories, but I'd love some.
Leah: I've got a [8] ______ in my bag. Here you are.

GRAMMAR Quantifiers

1 Complete the conversation with the words in the box.

a few how many how much
a little a lot lots of many much

Brad: Sorry, I'm late. There's [1] __________ traffic today.
Gina: No worries. Let's have a cup of tea.
Brad: Great!
Gina: [2] __________ sugar do you have in tea?
Brad: [3] __________. I love sugar!
Gina: [4] __________ teaspoons of sugar, then?
Brad: Five!
Gina: Really?! Oh, no! There isn't [5] __________ milk.
Brad: There's [6] __________. That's enough for us. Are there any biscuits?
Gina: Let's see. There aren't [7] __________ biscuits, but there are [8] __________ cupcakes. Would you like one?
Brad: Yes, please!

2 Read the text and circle the correct words.

This fruit is the durian, but how [1] **much / many** people in the UK know its name? Not [2] **a lot / a lot of**. That's because the durian is from Southeast Asia and only [3] **a few / a little** shops in the UK sell it. [4] **Lots / Many** people in Southeast Asia eat a durian every day, because they think it's good for them. Perhaps they don't know [5] how **much / many** sugar is in them. There's [6] **a lot / many**! There's one thing that everyone should know about the durian. It smells disgusting! In [7] **lots of / lot of** countries in Southeast Asia, you aren't allowed to eat durian in public places! What's my advice? Try [8] **bit / a bit of** durian when you see it, but don't forget to hold your nose!

3 Write sentences to describe the picture. Use *there is / are, a lot (of) / a few / a little* and the words in brackets.

1 (bread)
____
2 (tomatoes)
____
3 (olives)
____
4 (cheese)
____
5 (ham)
____
6 (orange juice)
____

4 Write questions with *how much / how many*.

1 space / be / there / in your bedroom
__________?
2 homework / you / do / at the weekend
__________?
3 fast food restaurants / be / there / in your town
__________?
4 dairy products / you / eat / every week
__________?
5 rain / your town / get / every year
__________?

5 Now write true answers for you to the questions in exercise 4. Use *a lot (of), lots (of), a few, a little* or *any*.

1 __________
2 __________
3 __________
4 __________
5 __________

EXTRA CHALLENGE

Look at the picture and correct the sentences.

1 There are four shelves.

____

2 There are a few plates.

____

3 There are some napkins.

____

4 There aren't any glasses.

____

5 There are a lot of bowls.

____

6 There are two knives.

____

WEBQUEST

Go online and find the answers to the questions.

1 Where does haggis come from?

____

2 What is haggis made of?

____

3 What is the name of someone who eats fish, but doesn't eat meat?

____

4 Where does the word "sandwich" come from?

____

5 What is in a BLT sandwich?

____

6 In Italy, people say 'salute' before they have a drink. What would you say in the UK?

____

PUZZLE

Copy every other letter to make a question. Then write true answers.

HDOBWIMRUNCJHLMOIHLWKCDNOFYLOBUSDVRMIANOK?

______________________________?

____

HEOSWVMPANNGYUVTECGREJTZALBULPEWSKDUOTYMOBULLYINKRE

______________________________?

____

IDSYTNHOEPRLEBALNRYCMIOLNGEPYKIWNPYLONUQRXBHAZG

______________________________?

____

AYRPENTLHWEVRBEMAZNLYBBTIGSLCTURIGTASOIWNTTPHXELCMUGPKBYOHAGRJD

______________________________?

____

INTERACTION Ordering food and drink

1 Answer the questions. Can you remember how to express yourself?

What do you say …

1 if you're a server in a café and you want to know what a customer wants from the menu?

______

2 to find out if the customer wants other things from the menu?

______

3 if you're in a café and you want to order a beef sandwich?

______

4 to find out the price of the sandwich?

______

5 when you give your money to the server?

______

2 9 Complete the dialogue with the correct words. Listen and check.

Server: 1 ______ I help 2 ______?

Client: 3 ______ like a banana smoothie, 4 ______.

Server: 5 ______ or small?

Client: Small, please.

Server: Anything to eat?

Client: 6 ______, that's 7 ______, thanks.

Server: 8 ______ £2.70.

Client: Here 9 ______ are. Three pounds.

Server: 10 ______ your change.

3 Read the dialogue and circle T (true) or F (false).

Debra: Hi. Can I have a muffin, please?

Server: Sure. Large or small?

Debra: Large, please.

Server: Anything else?

Debra: Yes, I'd also like a chocolate brownie, please. I'm starving! Are there any nuts in the brownie?

Server: Yes, I'm afraid there are.

Debra: Oh, I'm allergic to nuts. Are there any nuts in the muffins?

Server: No, there aren't.

Debra: Can I have two large muffins, then?

Server: OK. Anything else? Coffee? Fruit juice?

Debra: No, thanks. That's all.

Server: That's £3.40.

Debra: Here you are. Five pounds.

Server: That's £1.30 change.

1 Debra orders a large sandwich. T / F
2 She's very hungry so she orders two types of cakes. T / F
3 She can't eat nuts. T / F
4 Debra changes her order. T / F
5 She has something to drink. T / F
6 The server gives Debra the correct change. T / F

4 Complete the dialogue.

You: (Greet your customer and ask if you can help.)

1 ______

Lucas: Yes, please. I'd like a baguette, please.

You: (Find out what the customer wants in it.)

2 ______

Lucas: Roast beef and sundried tomatoes, please.

You: (Find out if the customer wants other things to eat from the menu.)

3 ______

Lucas: Yes, please. Can I have a slice of fruit cake, please?

You: (Find out if the customer wants a drink.)

4 ______

Lucas: A can of lemonade, please. How much is that?

You: (Tell the customer the price – £6.50.)

5 ______

Lucas: Here you are.

You: (Give the customer his change.)

6 ______

YOUR TURN TO SPEAK

5 10 Revise the *Express yourself* box on page 36 of the Student's Book. Then listen to the people and respond.

WRITING A magazine article

WRITING SKILL Prepositions of time: *on, at, in, before* & *after*

1 Circle the correct words.

1 When Jack gets home **on / at / after** school, he's hungry again.
2 **Finally / In / On** the middle of the evening, Jack has more food.
3 **In / On / At** eleven o'clock, he has a snack.
4 **On / After / Before** Saturday afternoons, he plays in a rugby match.
5 An hour **at / before / in** a training session, he has a special smoothie.

2 Complete the text with the sentences in exercise 1.

A food day in the life of a teenage rugby player

Fifteen-year-old Jack Powell goes to rugby practice twice a week and does exercise in the gym three times a week.
1 ______________________________ .

Jack eats a lot of food, but he has a healthy diet. The food he eats is very important. It gives him the energy to play rugby. This is a typical food day for Jack.

For breakfast, he has a large bowl of cereal, two slices of toast, a glass of orange juice and a cup of tea.
2 ______________________________ . This is usually a flapjack, a piece of fruit and a drink. For lunch, he has two ham or cheese sandwiches, some pieces of raw carrot, some nuts and a drink. He doesn't have anything sweet for dessert.

3 ______________________________ . He has a big glass of milk, some more nuts and another piece of fruit. 4 ______________________________ . There are bananas, milk and yoghurt in it. Jack has dinner half an hour after training. It's always steak, chicken or fish with lots of vegetables, but there's no dessert for him.
5 ______________________________ . It's another bowl of cereal, some more fruit, a few nuts, and a drink.

3 Read the text again and answer the questions.

1 How often does Jack go to the gym?
____
2 Why is it important for Jack to have a healthy diet?
____
3 What does he drink at breakfast time?
____
4 What time does he usually eat a flapjack?
____
5 How does Jack feel after school?
____
6 Does Jack have a dessert after dinner? What do you think the reason is?
____

4 Look at the *Writing Reference* on page 115. Then write an article about the food day in the life of a young sportsperson. Invent their personal details. Write about their:

– breakfast
– lunch
– dinner
– snacks

Reminder
- Check your prepositions of time.
- Check your countable and uncountable nouns.
- Check your quantifiers.

____

Review Units 1-3

VOCABULARY

1 Circle the word that doesn't belong to the group.

1	chicken	pasta	fork	butter
2	kayak	ice rink	tennis court	ski slope
3	niece	wife	cousin	friend
4	pear	spoon	plate	napkin
5	can	racket	bottle	jar
6	skate boarding	shopping	horse riding	mountain biking

2 Complete the sentences with the words in the box.

brush do get go play take

1 How often do you ______________ your teeth?
2 My grandparents never ______________ online.
3 I ______________ up at 7 o'clock.
4 We ______________ rugby once a week.
5 Does he ______________ out the rubbish?
6 Do they ______________ gymnastics at school?

3 Reorder the letters to complete the sentences.

1 I always wear a(n) ______________ on my bike. (**m t e l e h**)
2 ______________ contain sugar. (**s i c t u b i s**)
3 Is there a ______________ of wine in the fridge? (**t l o b t e**)
4 David is her second ______________. (**n b a s h d u**)
5 ______________ are my favourite fruit. (**r p g s a e**)
6 I think ______________ is boring. (**t o f b o l a l**)

GRAMMAR

4 Rewrite the sentences in the affirmative (+), negative (–) or interrogative (?).

1 He wakes up early.
(–) ______________
2 They aren't cooking dinner.
(?) ______________
3 Does she watch TV every day?
(+) ______________
4 I'm tidying my room.
(–) ______________
5 You don't enjoy surfing.
(?) ______________
6 He doesn't go skiing.
(?) ______________

5 Complete the sentences with the correct form of the verb. Use the present simple or present continuous.

1 We ______________ (have) a snack right now.
2 I usually ______________ (eat) fruit every morning.
3 Jack ______________ (not like) being outside.
4 My sister ______________ (do) sport twice a week.
5 I ______________ (not understand) the question.
6 Jenny ______________ (not swim) at the moment.

6 Circle the correct words.

1 There **isn't / aren't** any orange juice.
2 There's **not / no** pizza on the plate.
3 We haven't got **some / any** money.
4 I like **lot of / lots of** vegetables.
5 There are **a few / a little** people here.
6 How **much / many** cafés are there in town?

REVIEW CHECK

7 Read the text and choose the correct words.

Emma: This is my cousin, Zara. She's a fantastic swimmer and she [1] ... for the local swimming team.
Tim: How [2] ... times a week does she swim?
Emma: Six! Some of the sessions are before school, so she [3] ... at 5 o'clock in the morning. In this picture, she [4] ... butterfly and she [5] ... a swimming hat and goggles. She [6] ... them because she wants to swim as fast as possible. Zara is really hungry after training in the morning, so she [7] ... has an enormous breakfast.
Tim: How [8] ... does she eat?
Emma: A bowl of cereal with nuts, two [9] ... of toast with peanut butter, a banana, [10] ... egg sandwich with ham, and a glass of orange juice!

1
A swim **B** swims **C** is swimming
2
A often **B** much **C** many
3
A often gets up **B** gets up often **C** often get up
4
A swims **B** 's swimming **C** 's swiming
5
A 's wearing **B** isn't wearing **C** wears
6
A is always wearing **B** wears always **C** always wears
7
A never **B** hardly ever **C** always
8
A food **B** many **C** much
9
A slice **B** slices **C** piece
10
A any **B** a **C** an

Video

Ice hockey

BEFORE YOU WATCH

1 Read the introduction and the questions in NOW WATCH.

Introduction

Ice hockey is a very popular sport in Canada. Canada has some of the world's best players and thousands of Canadians go to watch their favourite teams play all over Canada and the USA.

NOW WATCH

2 Answer the questions.

1 Where was the first organized ice hockey game?

2 What do the initials NHL stand for?

3 What equipment do all players need?

4 What do you have to do to win a game of hockey?

5 What two adjectives does the narrator use at the end to describe ice hockey?

FOLLOW UP

3 Go online and find out about ice hockey. Write an interesting fact to share with your class.

Did you know that...?

4 Going places

READING

1 Read the texts. Where are they from?

A some postcards
B a travel brochure
C a geography book
D a social networking website

TRAVELLERS' TALES

1 

Leo

I climbed the Eiffel Tower today. Actually, that isn't completely true because you can't climb to the top. I walked up the 1,060 steps to the second level and then I got into the lift. The views of Paris were disappointing because it was cloudy. I took some photos anyway, but they were rubbish!

2 

Pablo & Sara

We had a weird experience today. We floated in the Dead Sea. There's so much salt in the water that you can't swim! Before getting in, we put mud over our bodies. When it was dry, we got into the water. It was lovely and warm, but Sara got some salt in her eye. Poor thing! It really hurt.

3 

Meg & Joe

We got up at dawn this morning. We met our guide, Jacques, and then got into his jeep. He drove us into the reserve. After 30 minutes, we stopped. We waited in silence and then suddenly we saw about 25 elephants. They were only metres from us. It was amazing. We took some fantastic photos.

4 

Vera

It was my first trip in a helicopter, so I was very nervous when we left Las Vegas. Forty-five minutes later, we flew over the Grand Canyon. It was awesome! Then we landed in the canyon. We got out of the helicopter, walked around and had a picnic. It's the best picnic place in the world!

5 

Alicia

I walked over the Sydney Harbour Bridge with my family today. It was scary! You can't take anything onto the bridge (not even a camera), so we left our things in a locker and we wore a special suit. The guide took a photo of us when we got onto the top of the bridge.

2 Match the countries in the box with the texts.

Australia France Israel South Africa The USA

1 ______________
2 ______________
3 ______________
4 ______________
5 ______________

3 Read the texts again and write the correct names.

1 Who got wet? ______________
2 Who put on different clothes? ______________
3 Who had bad weather? ______________
4 Who had something to eat? ______________
5 Who saw some wildlife? ______________
6 Who went by car? ______________
7 Who went on foot? ______________
8 Who travelled by air? ______________

WORD ZONE EXTRA

***get* + preposition**

4 Find the verb *get* in the texts and complete the definitions with the correct preposition.

1 We use *get* ______________ when we move into a position on something, e.g. the top of a bridge.
2 We use *get* ______________ when we go inside something, e.g. a car, a lift.
3 We use *get* ______________ when we go away from the inside of something, e.g. a car, a lift.

5 Answer the questions. Write true sentences for you.

1 Can you get out of bed quickly in the morning?

____

2 Do you get into bed at the same time every night?

____

3 Can you get onto a horse easily?

____

VOCABULARY Transport

6 Do the puzzle and find another form of transport.

1 A boat that you sail.
2 A ship that transports people and vehicles from one place to another.
3 A large vehicle that transports things by road.
4 You pay the driver to take you somewhere in this car.
5 A large vehicle that transports people long distances by road.
6 A large animal that you can ride.
7 A form of transport that goes by air.
8 Similar to a moped, but bigger and faster.
9 A system of trains that travel under the ground.
10 Public transport that travels on rails along the roads in a town / city.

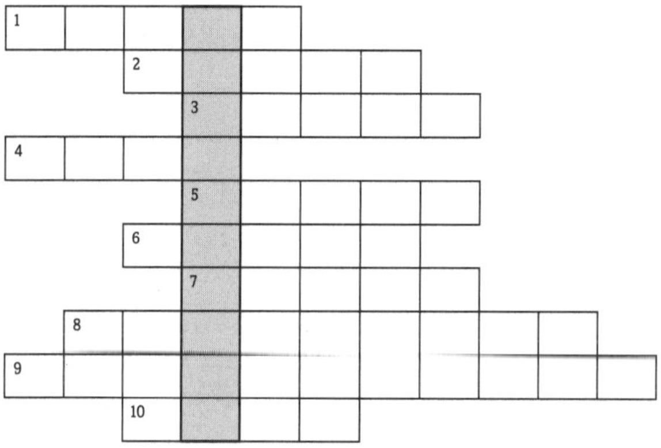

7 Complete the sentences with the words in the box.

bike bus hot-air balloon minibus van

1 We travelled over the Grand Canyon in a ____________.
2 I rode 40 km on my ______________ to raise money for charity.
3 They sat on the upper deck of the ______________ to get a good view of the city.
4 We phoned for a taxi, but a ______________ came. There was space for 10 people!
5 I went online and bought some food from a supermarket. They delivered it to my home in a ______________.

8 Write true sentences for you.

1 I love travelling by ______________ because ______________.
2 I don't like travelling by ______________ because ______________.
3 I don't want to go in a ______________ because ______________.

WANT TO KNOW MORE? Transport

9 Write the types of transport under the correct heading. Use a dictionary if you need to.

canoe carriage hang glider hovercraft rickshaw seaplane submarine

land

sea

air

10 Complete the adverts with the transport in exercise 9.

See the sights of Seville in a horse and [1] ______________!

Travelling to the Isle of Wight? Why don't you travel across the sea by [2] ______________ instead of the ferry? It's fast and exciting!

Go into a [3] ______________ at the maritime museum and imagine what it's like more than 250 metres under the sea!

The perfect present – a tandem flight in a [4] ______________. See what it's like to fly like a bird!

Don't take a taxi in London! Jump in a [5] ______________ instead. Our experienced riders can take you anywhere!

Go on a sightseeing tour by [6] ______________. We take off and land on the water. It's fun!

Hire a [7] ______________ and travel slowly down the river. It's quiet and relaxing.

GRAMMAR Past simple affirmative | *was* / *were*

1 Complete the dialogue with the correct past simple form of *be*.

Max: Where [1] ________ you this time last week?
Elena: I [2] ________ in London with my parents. We [3] ________ on holiday for five days.
Max: Really? [4] ________ it good?
Elena: It [5] ________ awesome, but the weather [6] ________ good. In fact, it [7] ________ terrible.
Max: Oh, no! What [8] ________ it like?
Elena: It [9] ________ cold and wet. There [10] ________ any sunny days. Not one!
Max: You [11] ________ unlucky. My sister and her friends [12] ________ in London last May and there [13] ________ a heatwave; 30° every day.
Elena: That's incredible. It [14] ________ like that for us!

2 Complete the tables with the verbs in the box. Write the correct past simple form.

~~arrive~~ leave love stop travel visit watch write

Regular		
+ ed	+d	double consonant + ed
	arrived	

Irregular

3 Complete the sentences with the past simple verbs in exercise 2.

1 They ________ at the cinema at 7.20pm and they ________ it three hours later.
2 My cousin ________ across Australia last year and he ________ an email to my aunt every day.
3 We ________ a brilliant film on TV last night, but my mum ________ watching it when it got scary!
4 I ________ some relatives when I was in New York last month. I ________ the city. It was amazing.

4 Complete the text with the past simple form of the verbs in the box.

buy decide feel get go have look say see walk

A big mistake

Last Saturday was 17th May. I [1] ________ up early that day because it was my mum's birthday and I [2] ________ no present for her. I [3] ________ to town by bus and [4] ________ in the shops for a few hours. In the end, I [5] ________ to get some chocolates and flowers for her. I also [6] ________ some big balloons. There wasn't space on the bus for the balloons, so I [7] ________ home. It takes 40 minutes on foot.
When I [8] ________ my mum, I [9] ________, 'Surprise! Happy Birthday!' She was very surprised because her birthday is actually May 27th. I [10] ________ very silly!

5 Circle the correct words to make time expressions.

1 **last / in / ago** Sunday
2 **at / on / in** the summer
3 two days **yesterday / ago / last**
4 **on / last / at** 8 o'clock last night
5 **in / yesterday / on** Thursday
6 **ago / last / in** night
7 **in / at / yesterday** afternoon
8 **on / in / at** Monday evening

6 Choose four time expressions from exercise 5. Write sentences about the things you or your family did then.

1 ________
____
2 ________
____
3 ________
____

LISTENING

1 Put the words in the box in the correct category. Use a dictionary if you need to.

catch a train change trains direct train high-speed train miss a train platform railway station signal failure train crash

Places connected to trains	Types of train

Verbs connected to trains	Problems that can affect a train

2 (11) Listen to a conversation. How many types of transport do you hear?

3 (11) Listen again and tick (✓) A, B or C.

1 Josh's mum tells her story because Josh… .
- A loves hearing it ☐
- B wants to go to Salamanca ☐
- C needs help with his homework ☐

2 She explains that she studied… .
- A Spanish at university in Wales ☐
- B English at university in Spain ☐
- C Welsh at university in England ☐

3 They planned to get to Salamanca via… .
- A Paris ☐
- B Manchester ☐
- C Madrid ☐

4 His mum missed the train from Waterloo because of… .
- A a train crash ☐
- B a signal failure ☐
- C a problem with her phone ☐

5 The next day, she caught… .
- A a flight to Madrid ☐
- B a train to Paris ☐
- C a coach to Salamanca ☐

6 Josh's mum… .
- A never arrived in Salamanca ☐
- B arrived in Salamanca before her friends ☐
- C met her friends when she arrived in Salamanca ☐

TEST YOUR MEMORY!

4 Answer the questions.

1 How old was Josh's mum in the story?

____

2 How long was the course at the summer school?

____

3 Where did she and her friends plan to meet at Waterloo Station?

____

4 How long did it take for her friends to get from London to Salamanca?

____

5 How long was the train journey from Madrid to Salamanca?

____

6 How did her friends feel when they saw Josh's mum?

____

5 Write these sentences in your language.

1 Really? That was good!

____

2 Guess what? I wasn't on the train.

____

3 You poor thing! Was it awful?

____

READING

1 Read the text quickly. Then complete the sentences with the correct word.

1 A ________________ is a person in the army.
2 A ________________ is a bag that you carry on your back.
3 To ________________ is to run very quickly.
4 A ________________ is a running machine.

It's no surprise that Mike Buss is called 'the Running Man'. On 24th September [1] ________________ , the ex-soldier completed a marathon (that's [2] ________________ miles and 385 yards or 42.195 Km) in 4 hours and 49 minutes. In doing so, Mike set a new world record. It was his 100th marathon in 100 consecutive days. Did he wear lightweight running gear for this last marathon? No, he didn't. He wore a pair of boots and he carried a 40 pound rucksack.

Over the [3] ________________ days, Mike travelled through 19 towns across the south of England. The 2,620 miles that he ran was equivalent to running around the coast of England, Scotland and Wales. At the end of the final challenge, Mike even had the energy to sprint across the finishing line at a speed of 7.5 miles/hour and finish the marathon at exactly [4] ________________ pm.

This wasn't Mike's first world record. In the same year, he broke the world record for running the longest distance on a treadmill in seven days; [5] ________________ miles or 832.255 Km. During that time, he had two hours of sleep a day and stopped for short times to eat and drink. How much weight did he lose? [6] ________________ pounds and 6 ounces. That's over half a stone!

So why does he do it? Many people run marathons to raise money for charity and Mike is no different. He decided to start running when he left the army and every year he raises tens of thousands of pounds for charities that help British soldiers and their families.

100 g = 3.53 ounces	*500 g = 1.1 pounds*
6.35kg = 1 stone	*1.609 Km = 1 mile*

2 Complete the text with the numbers in the box.

8 26 100 517.25 2010 12.30

3 Read the text again and tick (✓) YES or NO.

	YES	NO
1 When Mike ran 100 marathons, he didn't run at weekends.	☐	☐
2 Mike ran around the whole of the UK in 100 days.	☐	☐
3 In his last marathon, his rucksack was heavy.	☐	☐
4 He sprinted for 2,620 miles.	☐	☐
5 Mike has more than one world record.	☐	☐
6 He stopped every two hours when he was on the treadmill.	☐	☐
7 Mike isn't in the army anymore.	☐	☐
8 He runs marathons to help other people.	☐	☐

WORD ZONE EXTRA

Measurements of mass

4 Complete the table with words from the text.

Metric units of mass
We measure mass in grams (g) and kilograms (kg).

Non-metric units of mass
We measure mass in [1] ________________ (oz) and [2] ________________ (lb).
There are 14lbs in a [3] ________________ .
In the UK, we usually use this measurement for people's weight.

5 Think about the mass of the words in brackets. Write three sentences.

1 (an apple / non-metric unit)
An apple weighs ________________
2 (you / metric unit)
____
3 (a bag of sugar / non-metric unit)
____

VOCABULARY Prepositions of movement

Prepositions of movement

6 **Look at the picture and complete the words.**

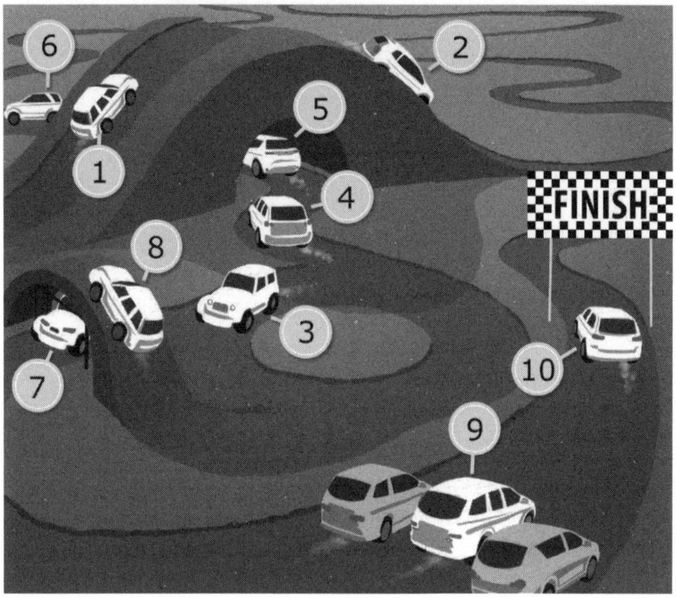

1 u_	6 a___ f___
2 d___	7 u____
3 a_____	8 o___
4 i___	9 b_______
5 t_______	10 t_______

7 **Complete the text with the words in the box.**

across along around between through under up

The English Channel separates the UK from France. In the past, for people who hated flying, the only way to travel [1] __________ the two countries was by ferry. Ferries still take passengers [2] __________ the English Channel, but now you can travel [3] __________ it in the Channel Tunnel. The Eurostar is a high-speed passenger train that travels [4] __________ the Channel Tunnel at 160 km/hour. It only takes two hours 15 minutes to travel from London to Paris. So, in less than three hours, you can walk [5] __________ the Avenue des Champs-Élysées, walk [6] __________ the Luxembourg Gardens or climb [7] __________ the Eiffel Tower to the top.

WANT TO KNOW MORE?

Ways of moving

8 **Match verbs 1–6 with definitions A-F. Use a dictionary if you need to.**

1 hop
2 skip
3 crawl
4 stroll
5 creep
6 march

A to walk leisurely
B to jump from one foot to the other
C to walk quickly like a soldier
D to jump on one leg
E to move on your hands and knees like a baby
F to move slowly and quietly

1 _ 2 _ 3 _ 4 _ 5 _ 6 _

9 **Complete the sentences with the verbs in exercise 8.**

1 We've got nothing to do. Let's __________ around the park for an hour.
2 Hopscotch is a children's game where you __________ __________ and jump along some spaces on the ground.
3 Sssh! __________ up the stairs and don't wake the baby!
4 He can't walk yet. He can only __________.
5 Young children often __________ along the pavement when they're happy.
6 Don't __________ down the road! We aren't in a hurry.

10 **Imagine your teacher is taking you and your class to an obstacle course. Describe what you have to do. Use prepositions of movement and the words in the box.**

bars ladder ropes tunnel

____
____
____
____
____
____
____
____
____
____

GRAMMAR Past simple negative & questions

1 Rewrite the sentences. Make them negative.

TV presenter Helen Skelton completes her expedition to the South Pole – on skis, kite skis and an ice bike.

1 She travelled by car.
____

2 She rode a normal bike.
____

3 She ate fresh food.
____

4 She wore a wetsuit.
____

5 I saw her on TV.
____

6 Her journey took 18 months.
____

7 She sent a postcard from the South Pole.
____

2 Reorder the words and write questions. Then match them with the answers in the box.

Thousands of pounds. A Norwegian explorer. Yes, she became ill. 800km. In tents and sleeping bags.

1 how far / travel / did / Helen
_______________?
____

2 she / who / go / with / did
_______________?
____

3 sleep / did / they / where
_______________?
____

4 have /did / Helen / problems / any
_______________?
____

5 money / she / did / how much / raise
_______________?
____

3 Complete the conversation. Use the correct past simple form of the verbs in brackets.

Tania: [1] _______________ (you / do) your homework last night?
Martin: No, I [2] _______________ (watch) a fantastic TV programme with my sister. It was about Helen Skelton.
Tania: Who?
Martin: You know, the TV presenter who [3] _______________ (go) on an expedition to the South Pole last January.
Tania: I'm not sure who she is.
Martin: We [4] _______________ (not know) anything about her before the programme. She's amazing. She [5] _______________(kayak) down the River Amazon a few years ago.
Tania: Really? Well, I [6] _______________ (not watch) TV last night. I was out.
Martin: Who [7] _______________ (you / meet)?
Tania: Jake, Sally and Max. We [8] _______________ (play) tennis in the park until it started raining.
Martin: What was the score?
Tania: 6–4 to Sally and me!

4 Complete the past simple questions with the verbs in the box. Then read the dialogue again in exercise 3 and write the correct short answer.

enjoy know rain stay win

1 ___________ Martin ___________ at home last night?
____

2 ___________ Martin and his sister ___________ watching the programme?
____

3 ___________ Tania ___________ about Helen Skelton?
____

4 ___________ it ___________ last night?
____

5 ___________ Jake and Max ___________ the match?
____

5 What did you and your family do last night? Include affirmative and negative sentences.

____
____
____
____
____

EXTRA CHALLENGE

Imagine that one of your friends went to Marrakech last week. Write a dialogue between you and your friend and ask about his / her experiences. Use the list below to help you. Use some of the expressions in the *Express yourself* box on 47 of the Student's Book to show interest.

Things to do in Marrakech

- *Stay in a Moroccan riad*
- *Stroll around the souk and buy Moroccan products*
- *Try Moroccan food such as couscous*
- *Visit the Cascades d'Ouzoud*
- *Go on a trek in the Atlas Mountains*

WEBQUEST

Go online and find the answers to the questions.

1 What language do they speak in Iceland? How do you say *hello* and *goodbye*?

____

2 What is unusual about surnames in Iceland?

____

3 In which three countries are the Atlas Mountains?

____

4 What is the highest point in the Atlas Mountains? How high is it?

____

5 What did Thor Heyerdahl name his boat the *Kon-Tiki* after?

____

6 In which country did Thor Heyerdahl die?

____

PUZZLE

Find eleven verbs in the maze. Which two verbs don't change spelling in the affirmative past simple?

____

____

____

____

____

____

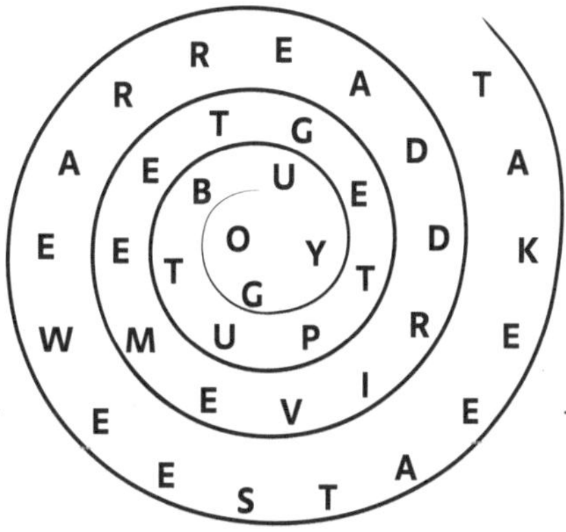

____

____

____

____

____

____

4

INTERACTION Travelling around

1 Answer the questions. Can you remember how to express yourself?

What do you say ...

1 to know if the bus goes to your destination (Oxford)?
____

2 to find out the length of a journey?
____

3 to know if it's cheaper for students?
____

4 to find out the time of the next train?
____

5 to know the platform that the train leaves from?
____

2 (12) Complete the exchanges with the correct words. Listen and check.

Passenger 1: What [1] _______________ is the [2] _______________ bus to Poppleton?
Passenger 2: In 10 minutes.

Passenger: [3] _______________ I have a ticket to Bristol, [4] _______________?
Clerk: [5] _______________ or return?
Passenger: A return, please.

Clerk: Have you [6] _______________ a railcard?
Passenger: No, I [7] _______________.
Clerk: Are you [8] _______________ 16?
Passenger: No, I'm [9] _______________. I'm 15.

3 Read the dialogue and complete the summary.

Clerk: Can I help you?
Ben: Yes, a ticket to Brighton, please.
Clerk: Single or return?
Ben: Return, please.
Clerk: That's £16.80.
Ben: Is there a student reduction?
Clerk: Yes, there is. Have you got your railcard?
Ben: Yes, I have. Here it is.
Clerk: That's great. That's £13.50 then.
Ben: It's 10.05 now. What time is the next train?
Clerk: There's one at 10.20 from Platform 5.
Ben: Thanks. How long does the journey take?
Clerk: It's about an hour, I think. Let's see. Yes, the 10.20 arrives in Brighton at 11.17.
Ben: Thanks. Bye.

Ben buys a [1] _______________ ticket to [2] _______________. The ticket normally costs [3] _______________, but Ben pays [4] _______________ because he's a [5] _______________ and he's got a [6] _______________. Ben's train leaves from [7] _______________ in [8] _______________ minutes.

4 Complete the dialogue.

You: (Ask if the bus goes to Warrington.)
1 _______________
Driver 1: No, it doesn't. You need the 101 over there.
You: (Ask for a single ticket to Warrington.)
2 _______________
Driver 2: Are you under 16?
You: (Say yes and tell him your age – 14.)
3 _______________
Driver 2: That's £1.80.
You: (Ask the driver to tell you when you're there.)
4 _______________
Driver 2: Sure. No problem.
You: (Ask how long the journey takes.)
5 _______________
Driver 2: About 35 minutes. Here's your ticket.
You: (Thank the driver.)
6 _______________
Driver 2: No worries.

YOUR TURN TO SPEAK

5 (13) Revise the *Express yourself* box on page 48 of the Student's Book. Then listen to the people and respond.

WRITING A holiday blog

WRITING SKILL Sequencing words and expressions

1 Reorder the words and write sentences.

1 went / we / after that / the London Eye / on

____

2 I / to / listened / and then / my iPod

____

3 found / first / seats / we / our

____

4 we / went / left and / finally / home

____

5 had / we / then / breakfast / some

____

6 flight gallery / visited / we / the / first

____

2 Complete the blog with the sentences in exercise 1.

Daisy's blog
A day trip to London

We got up really early yesterday morning and Dad drove us to the station for the 7.05 train to London. It arrived on time and we got on quickly. 1 ______________________________ . My seat faced the wrong way so I travelled backwards. I didn't like it but nobody wanted to change seats. 2 ______________________________ . I was starving so I ordered two egg sandwiches and a cup of hot chocolate. After that, I read a magazine 3 ______________________________ .

I was really excited when we got to London. First, we went by underground to Waterloo Station. Then, we walked along the Embankment next to the River Thames. 4 ______________________________ . It's a 135-metre-high wheel that travels round slowly. The views of London were awesome. I saw lots of famous places.

After lunch, we went to the Science Museum. 5 ______________________________ . We saw some really old planes. One of them was the first plane to fly non-stop across the Atlantic in June 1919. It took 16 hours! Then, we went to the Space gallery and saw some real space rockets. After that, we watched a 3D film in the IMAX cinema. It was amazing. 6 ______________________________ . We were tired but really happy.

3 Read the blog again and answer the questions.

1 Why was Daisy unhappy with her seat?

____

2 How did they get to Waterloo Station?

____

3 How high is the London Eye?

____

4 Where did they go in the afternoon?

____

5 How long did the first flight across the Atlantic take?

____

6 What type of film did they see?

____

4 Look at the *Writing Reference* on page 116. Then write a blog post about a day trip to an interesting city. Invent the things you did and the things you saw. Write about:

– the journey
– sightseeing
– museum visits

Reminder

- Check your past simple forms, especially the irregular verbs.
- Check your prepositions of movement.
- Check your sequencing words.

____

5 Out of this world

READING

1 What do you know about astronomy? Match names 1–5 with A–E. Then read the text and check.

1 Galileo	A one of Jupiter's moons
2 Callisto	B a German astronomer
3 Herschel	C a telescope
4 Uranus	D an Italian astronomer
5 Hubble	E a planet

1_ 2_ 3_ 4_ 5_

2 Read the text again. Circle the centuries it refers to.

16th 17th 18th 19th 20th 21st

THE TELESCOPE

The 400th anniversary of the birth of modern astronomy was in 2009. Four centuries earlier in Italy, Galileo had looked up at the sky at night through his home-made telescope. Later, he discovered the four largest moons of Jupiter (Io, Ganymede, Callisto and Europa) and saw craters on the Moon. As astronomy became more popular, astronomers wanted to see further and deeper into space so they built bigger and better telescopes.

William Herschel, a German musician who came to England in the middle of the 18th century, made his own telescopes too. He surprised everyone when he discovered a new planet in the solar system through one of them – Uranus. Nobody thought that there was a planet further away than Saturn. Astronomers around the world celebrated the bicentenary of this discovery in 1981. In the past, telescopes were not as powerful as they are nowadays and they were always on Earth. Today, the Hubble Telescope is a telescope that orbits the Earth and sends back thousands of incredible images to astronomers on the ground. Its position means that astronomers can see further into space than ever before. What would Galileo and Herschel think about that?

3 Read the text again and circle the correct answers.

1 Modern astronomy started in … .
A 1509 B 1609 C 2009

2 Galileo … a telescope.
A borrowed B bought C made

3 Astronomers improved telescopes in order to … .
A see more distant things B see closer things C travel in space

4 People knew about Uranus … Saturn.
A before B after C at the same time as

5 Herschel discovered Uranus in … .
A 1781 B 1881 C 1981

6 The Hubble Telescope is … .
A on Earth B on the Moon C in space

EXTRA WORD ZONE

Celebrations of periods of time

4 Find the words in the text to complete the definitions.

1 An ____________________ is a day or a year that is one year or a number of years after an event.

2 A ____________________ is a day or a year that is 200 years after an event.

5 Write two sentences using the words in exercise 4.

1 ____

____

2 ____

____

VOCABULARY Adjectives

6 Rewrite the sentences using the opposite adjectives.

1 Astronomy isn't boring.

____

2 The students weren't quiet.

____

3 It isn't cheap to eat here.

____

4 The river didn't look shallow.

____

5 You aren't late.

____

6 The bus wasn't empty.

____

7 We don't live in a dangerous area.

____

8 It wasn't a fast train.

____

7 Complete the text with the adjectives in the box.

beautiful expensive popular short soft thick

My Shar Pei

Dogs are 1 ______________ pets in the UK with over 7.3 million dog owners. We've got a Shar Pei. Its name means 'sand skin' in Chinese because its skin isn't 2 ______________ to touch. Shar Pei puppies have got 3 ______________ legs and lots of 4 ______________ skin on their face that looks like wrinkles. The puppies are 5 ______________ to buy – between £500 and £1000. Some people think these dogs are really ugly, but we think our Shar Pei is 6 ______________ !

8 Describe the street where you live and the area it is in. Use the adjectives in exercise 6.

____

____

____

____

____

WANT TO KNOW MORE? Adjectives

9 Read the sentences and try to understand the adjectives in bold. Then match them with the opposites in the box. Use a dictionary if you need to.

common dark dirty low rough

1 One day every month the Moon is very **high** in the sky.

____

2 The part of the Moon that we see is the **bright** part.

____

3 The surface of the Moon doesn't look **smooth**.

____

4 A full Moon looks **clean** and white.

____

5 Some people think that a full Moon causes **strange** events.

____

10 Circle the correct words.

1 Dogs are a **common** / **dark** pet in the UK.
2 Take off your shoes! They're really **low** / **dirty**.
3 It's **rough** / **dark** in here. I can't see anything.
4 That's **low** / **strange**. My bag was on my desk and now it isn't.
5 My dog's ears are soft and **smooth** / **bright**.
6 I like it when my bedroom is **strange** / **clean** and tidy.
7 The shelf is very **high** / **dark**. I can't reach it.
8 Don't look at the sun! It's very **common** / **bright**.
9 Ouch! That hurts. It's very **rough** / **clean**.
10 It's a **dark** / **low** chair because it's for a young child.

11 Write true sentences for you using some of the adjectives in exercise 9.

____

____

____

____

____

GRAMMAR Comparatives | *not as … as* | *less*

1 Write the comparatives.

1 beautiful *more beautiful than*
2 dry ______
3 wide ______
4 dangerous ______
5 short ______
6 bad ______
7 early ______
8 wet ______
9 soft ______
10 late ______

2 Complete the text with the comparative form of the adjectives.

Tips for young astronomers

- Start with some binoculars. They're [1] ______ (cheap) than telescopes.
- Binoculars are [2] ______ (easy) to use because they're [3] ______ (small) and [4] ______ (light).
- Telescopes are [5] ______ (big), [6] ______ (heavy) and less portable.
- You can carry binoculars around your neck. It's [7] ______ (safe) than carrying a large telescope.
- You can see [8] ______ (far) through a telescope than binoculars, but you get a [9] ______ (narrow) view, so it's [10] ______ (difficult) to find objects in the sky.

3 Complete the sentences with the comparative form of the adjectives in the box.

heavy high hot short

1 Everest is ______ Mulhacén.
2 The weather in Spain is ______ in Iceland.
3 The Ebro is ______ the Amazon.
4 A kilogram is ______ 10 grams.

4 Rewrite the sentences so that they mean the same. Use *not as … as* and *less*.

1 Winter is colder than summer.
Summer isn't ______
2 A car isn't as expensive as a house.
A car is ______
3 Dogs are more interesting than cats.
Cats aren't ______
4 Football is more popular than cricket.
Cricket isn't ______
5 My bed isn't as comfortable as yours.
My bed is ______

5 Complete the dialogue with the correct comparative form of the adjectives in brackets.

Zac: What's that?
Oliver: It's the International Space Station.
Zac: It's very big.
Oliver: It's a bit [1] ______ (big) than a football pitch, but the space where the astronauts live isn't [2] ______ (large) as you imagine. I'd love to go there.
Zac: But that's impossible.
Oliver: No, it isn't. In 2009, a Canadian man called Guy Laliberté visited the space station as a space tourist. It was [3] ______ (expensive) than other holidays – he paid $35 million to go.
Zac: That's incredible. He's obviously [4] ______ (rich) than us! What did he do there?
Oliver: It wasn't [5] ______ (relaxing) as normal holidays. He helped the astronauts with their experiments.
Zac: That's [6] ______ (interesting) than my holidays! We always go to the same place every year.
Oliver: It's [7] ______ (good) than staying at home!
Zac: I suppose so.

6 Write five sentences comparing you and a friend.

1 ______
2 ______
3 ______
4 ______
5 ______

LISTENING

1 Complete the definitions with the words in the box. Use a dictionary if you need to.

climate greenhouse humid
rainforest temperate tropical

1	______________________ ,	*n.* A building that is hotter than normal where you grow plants.
2	______________________ ,	*adj.* Containing a lot of water: a ~ atmosphere.
3	______________________ ,	*n.* A forest in a tropical area where there is a lot of rain.
4	______________________ ,	*n.* The type of weather in a region / country.
5	______________________ ,	*adj.* Describing parts of the world where the climate is hot and wet: a ~ island.
6	______________________ ,	*adj.* Describing a climate that isn't very hot or cold.

2 14 Listen to a conversation. What is the Eden Project?

A a museum B a 3D cinema C a tourist attraction D a school

3 14 Listen again and complete the summary with the correct information.

The Eden Project

The largest indoor [1] ______________________ in the world is at the Eden Project.

There are two [2] ______________ called Biomes – the Rainforest Biome and the Mediterranean Biome.

It's hotter and more [3] ______________ in the Rainforest Biome.

You get an amazing [4] ______________ over the rainforest from the Lookout.

There isn't a [5] ______________ to the Lookout. You go up some stairs.

It's [6] ______________ to get your tickets to the Eden Project online.

For children who arrive on foot, by bike or public transport, it's [7] ______________ to enter.

Lucy and her dad decide to go by [8] ______________ .

TEST YOUR MEMORY!

4 Answer the questions.

1 When does Lucy's dad want to visit the Eden Project?

____

2 What is the world's largest rainforest? Where is it?

____

3 How high is the Lookout?

____

4 What is the temperature on the Lookout?

____

5 How much does a normal ticket for children cost?

____

5 Write these sentences in your language.

1 No way, Dad! I'm not into plants.

____

2 Come on, Lucy. It'll be good.

____

3 Come on, hurry!

____

5 READING

1 Look at the photos. Where do you think they are? Read the text quickly and find the names of the places.

1 At 5,895 metres, Kilimanjaro in Tanzania is the highest mountain in Africa. Most people believe that its name comes from the Swahili words for 'white mountain'. That's because the top of Kilimanjaro is covered in an ice cap. However, this is 80% smaller than in 1912 and experts believe the mountain could have no ice and snow in the next 20 years.

2 Kilimanjaro lies 330 km south of the Equator and it comprises three volcanoes. Two of them, Mawenzi and Shira are extinct. The highest one, Kibo, is dormant, so it could erupt again. It last erupted 360,000 years ago, but its most recent volcanic activity was only 200 years ago. The highest point on Kilimanjaro is called Uhuru Peak, on the edge of Kibo's crater.

3 Every year about 25,000 people try to go up Kilimanjaro. It isn't something you can do on your own. Local guides lead groups of people along one of the six routes to the summit and porters carry your equipment. You need to be fit to take on the challenge, but you don't need any special climbing experience. However, about two-thirds of people don't succeed, usually because of altitude sickness.

4
- The fastest time to climb Kilimanjaro was 5 hours, 38 minutes and 40 seconds by an Italian, Bruno Brunod, in 2001.
- The oldest person to climb Kilimanjaro was a Frenchman named Valtee Daniel. He was 87!

2 Match headings A–D with paragraphs 1–4.

A More than a mountain
B Record breakers
C The roof of Africa
D Too much for some

1 __ 2 __ 3 __ 4 __

3 Read the text again and tick YES if the sentence is true or NO if the sentence is false.

	YES	NO
1 Kilimanjaro is the highest mountain in the world.	☐	☐
2 There is less ice on top of the mountain than in the past.	☐	☐
3 Mawenzi and Shira are dangerous volcanoes.	☐	☐
4 Uhuru Peak is at the bottom of a volcano.	☐	☐
5 There's only one way to the top of the mountain.	☐	☐
6 People often become ill because they're high up.	☐	☐
7 It took Bruno Brunod just over five and a half hours to get to Uhuru Peak.	☐	☐
8 You can't go up Kilimanjaro when you're elderly.	☐	☐

WORD ZONE EXTRA

Latitude

4 Write the words in the box in the correct place.

the Antarctic Circle the Arctic Circle the Equator the North Pole the South Pole

90° North
1 ______

66° North
2 ______

0°
3 ______

66° South
4 ______

90° South
5 ______

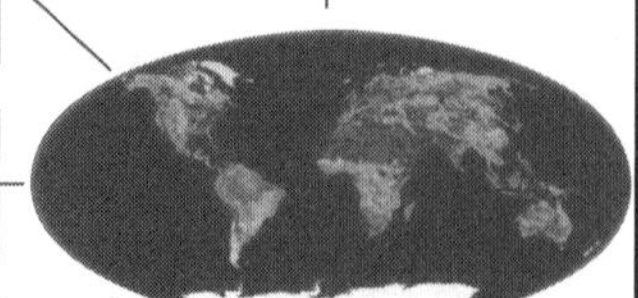

VOCABULARY Landscapes

5 Complete the words.

1 The Sahara is a d _ _ _ _ _ .
2 Mont Blanc is a m _ _ _ _ _ _ _ .
3 The Pyrenees is a m _ _ _ _ _ _ _ _ r_ _ _ _ .
4 Vesuvius is a v _ _ _ _ _ _ .
5 Ibiza is an i _ _ _ _ _ .
6 The Mediterranean is a s _ _ .
7 Loch Ness is a l _ _ _ in Scotland.
8 The Nile is a r_ _ _ _ .

6 Complete the definitions with the words in the box.

beach coastline farmland forest
hill plain stream valley

1 A ______________ is an area of land with lots of trees.
2 ______________ is land that people use for farming.
3 The ______________ is the area of land next to the sea.
4 A ______________ is the low land between two hills.
5 A ______________ is a large flat area of land with few trees.
6 A ______________ is a high area of land.
7 A ______________ is a small narrow river.
8 A ______________ is an area of sand next to the sea.

7 Write three true sentences about the location of a river, a mountain and an island in your country.

1 ______________

2 ______________

3 ______________

WANT TO KNOW MORE?
Adjectives to describe landscapes

8 Complete the sentences with the words in the box. Use a dictionary if you need to.

agricultural arid fertile
mountainous rocky wooded

Deserts are often separated from the sea by a [1] ______________ region. They are very [2] ______________ places because there is little water. The ground is [3] ______________ , so it is difficult for plants to grow. Sometimes there is an oasis in the desert. This is a [4] ______________ place where there is water. They are often [5] ______________ with palm trees. There are [6] ______________ areas too. People grow food there.

9 Circle the correct words.

1 It's difficult to walk along the **rocky** / **fertile** coastline.
2 They sell **agricultural** / **arid** products on that farm.
3 Switzerland is a **mountainous** / **rocky** country.
4 There are lots of different trees in the **wooded** / **agricultural** valley.
5 They grow all their food on the **fertile** / **arid** plain.
6 It doesn't rain much in an **arid** / **rocky** climate.

10 Write sentences comparing things. Use some of the adjectives in exercise 8.

1 two cities you've visited
____

2 the north and the south of your country
____

3 two countries
____

GRAMMAR Superlatives | *the least*

1 Write the superlatives.

1 heavy *the heaviest*
2 far ____________
3 wide ____________
4 dangerous ____________
5 short ____________
6 bad ____________
7 early ____________
8 hot ____________
9 soft ____________
10 late ____________
11 interesting ____________
12 good ____________

2 Circle the correct words.

This version of *The Scream* by Edvard Munch was sold at auction for $120 million in May 2012. Measuring 91 x 73.5 cm, it isn't [1] **largest / the most largest / the largest** painting in the world, but it's definitely one of the [2] **famous / most famous / famousest**. It isn't the [3] **happyest / happiest / happier** subject matter – it shows the face of someone in torment. However, of the four versions of *The Scream*, this one is [4] **the brightest / the most brightest / most brightest** and [5] **the colourfullest / most colourful / the most colourful**.

3 Complete the sentences with *the most* or *the least* and the adjectives in the box.

dangerous exciting intelligent popular

1 He has no friends. He's ____________ boy in the class.
2 You always get top marks. You're ____________ person I know.
3 It's ____________ road in the town. There are lots of accidents here.
4 I fell asleep in that film. It was ____________ film I have ever seen.

4 Complete the text with the adjectives in brackets. Use comparatives and superlatives.

Elephants are [1] ____________ (big) land mammals in the world. They've also got [2] ____________ (large) brains in the animal kingdom, but that doesn't mean that they're [3] ____________ (intelligent) animal of them all.
Adult male African elephants can be almost four metres tall and weigh about 6,990 kg. Adult Indian elephants aren't [4] ____________ (tall) or [5] ____________ (heavy) as that. Their ears are [6] ____________ (small) than those of African elephants too.
One of [7] ____________ (soft) parts on an elephant's skin is called the knuckle and it's behind the ears. The knuckle is [8] ____________ (sensitive) than other parts and elephant trainers give commands by touching it.
Despite the size of elephants' ears, their hearing is [9] ____________ (bad) than other animals. Their eyesight isn't [10] ____________ (good) as other animals either because their eyes are very small. Elephants are probably one of [11] ____________ (hungry) animals in the world. They spend about 16 hours a day eating and they eat about 225 kg of food!
Female elephants are [12] ____________ (sociable) than males and live in groups with their mothers, daughters, sisters and aunts.

5 Write sentences comparing the things in the lists. Use comparatives and superlatives.

1 rats dogs horses cheetahs
____
____

2 computer games films books magazines
____
____

3 Spain Canada Russia the UK
____
____

EXTRA CHALLENGE

Imagine that you are about to climb up Kilimanjaro with a local guide. You can take up to four items with you. Write a dialogue between you and a friend in which you try to agree on which items to take. Use some of the expressions in the *Express yourself* box on page 57 of the Student's Book to make suggestions, give reasons, agree and disagree.

camera compass first-aid kit
food helmet map mobile phone
MP3 player oxygen paper and pen
rope sunglasses warm hat water

WEBQUEST

Go online and find the answers to the questions.

1 In Roman mythology, what is Neptune the god of?

2 What is the largest volcano in the solar system? Where is it?

3 Who was the first person to climb to the top of Everest? What was the year?

4 What's the largest desert in Australia?

5 What's the address of the British Museum? What are the two nearest underground stations?

6 How many days a year is the Natural History Museum open?

PUZZLE

Reorder the letters to make comparatives and superlatives. Then answer the questions.

What's the ***gibtseg*** ______ planet in the solar system? ______

What's the ***eontlgs*** ______ river in the world? ______

Are humans ***rome teglinitnel*** ______ than animals? ______

What's the ***evaihste*** ______ mammal in the world? ______

Is it ***lrodec*** ______ in Antarctica than in the Arctic? ______

INTERACTION Buying things

1 Answer the questions. Can you remember how to express yourself?

What do you say ...

1 to find out the price of the postcards?

____

2 to ask to see a telescope in a display case?

____

3 to find out if your customer wants a bag?

____

2 15 Complete the exchanges with the correct words. Listen and check.

Shop assistant: 1 __________ I help you?
Customer: Yes, 2 __________ like one of those key rings, please.
Shop assistant: Can you show me 3 __________ one?
Customer: That blue one, please.
Shop assistant: 4 __________ be £2.4x0.

Customer: Have you got 5 __________ posters of dinosaurs?
Shop assistant: Yes, we have.
Customer: 6 __________ that one with the Brontosaurus on it, please?
Shop assistant: I'm sorry, we've sold 7 __________ of those.

Customer: Can I pay 8 __________ these three magnets, please?
Shop assistant: That's £10.00.
Customer: Really? How 9 __________ are they?
Shop assistant: They're £3.50 each or three for £10.00.

3 Read the dialogue and circle T (true) or F (false).

Shop assistant: Can I help you?
Maria: I'd like a mug, please. It's for my dad.
Shop assistant: The mugs are over here. We've got lots of different ones.
Maria: How much are they?
Shop assistant: It depends. Some are more expensive than others. That one with elephants on it is hand-painted, so it's £10.99.
Maria: I need something cheaper than that. Have you got any with planets on them? My dad's into astronomy.
Shop assistant: Yes, we have. We've got one with the Moon, one with Mars and one with Jupiter.
Maria: Can I have the one with Jupiter, please? It's the most colourful one.
Shop assistant: Sure. That'll be £4.99.
Maria: Here you are.
Shop assistant: Here's your receipt and change.
Maria: Thanks. Bye.

1 Maria wants to buy some mugs. T / F
2 The mugs are all the same price. T / F
3 Maria doesn't want the mug with elephants on it. T / F
4 Maria's dad is interested in planets. T / F
5 The Jupiter mug is brighter than the other two. T / F
6 Maria doesn't get any change. T / F

4 Complete the dialogue.

You: (Ask to help the customer.)
1 ______________________________
Customer: I'd like to buy a key ring, please.
You: (Ask the customer to show you the exact one.)
2 ______________________________
Customer: Can I have one like that, but in red?
You: (Apologise and explain that you haven't got any more red ones.)
3 ______________________________
Customer: OK. Can I have a green one, please?
You: (Tell the customer the price – £4.25.)
4 ______________________________
Customer: Here you are.
You: (Ask if the customer wants a bag.)
5 ______________________________
Customer: No, thanks.

YOUR TURN TO SPEAK

5 16 Revise the *Express yourself* box on page 58 of the Student's Book. Then listen to the people and respond.

WRITING A description of a region

WRITING SKILL Giving examples

1 Complete the extracts from the Snowdonia text with the words in the box.

beach holidays kayaking perch rivers a torch

1 "such as ____________ and brown trout"
2 "including walking, climbing, cycling, horse-riding and ____________"
3 "for example in school ____________"
4 including mountains, valleys, forests, ____________ ____________ and lakes"
5 "such as warm clothes, ____________, some water and sugary snacks"
6 "for example Criccieth ____________"

2 Complete the text with the examples and lists in exercise 1.

Snowdonia

At 1,085 m, Snowdon is the highest mountain in England and Wales. It also gives its name to the National Park around it, Snowdonia. Situated in the north-west of Wales, Snowdonia is the largest of Wales' three National Parks. Its landscape is beautiful and varied, [1] ____________ ____________.

One of these lakes, Bala Lake (Llyn Tegid in Welsh), is the largest natural lake in Wales. It is home to a lot of fish, [2] ____________.

Snowdonia has also got a long coastline with lots of fantastic beaches. Some are rocky, [3] ____________ ____________, but most are wide and sandy like Black Rock Sands or Barmouth.

It is no surprise that about eight million people visit Snowdonia every year. There is a variety of outdoor activities to do, [4] ____________.

For something less physical, there are some beautiful villages to visit like Betws y Coed and Beddgelert.

Every year, lots of people climb up Snowdon. You do not need to be an experienced climber, but it is important to wear walking shoes and to take things with you, [5] ____________ ____________.

An easier way to get to the top is by train. The Snowdon Mountain Railway operates every day from March to October. It can get very busy at certain times [6] ____________ ____________, so you should book your tickets early.

3 Read the text again and circle the correct answers.

1 Snowdonia National Park is named after a **lake / river / mountain**.
2 Wales has got **two / three / four** National Parks.
3 Black Rock Sands isn't as **rocky / sandy / wide** as Criccieth Beach.
4 Beddgelert is a Welsh **city / town / village**.
5 **Anyone / Only people with walking shoes / Only people with experience** can climb Snowdon.
6 You can go up Snowdon by train **all year / for 6 months / for 8 months**.

4 Look at the Writing Reference on page 117. Then write a text about a National Park. Invent the details if necessary and include some examples and lists. Write about:

– the landscape
– important places
– tourist attractions

Reminder
- Check your comparative and superlative forms.
- Check how you introduce examples and lists.

____
____
____
____
____
____
____
____
____
____
____
____
____
____
____
____
____
____
____
____

6 Crime watch

READING

1 Read the article quickly. Match the words and the definitions.

1 empty-handed
2 mugshot
3 have a sweet tooth
4 tracks

A marks on the ground from a person / vehicle
B without getting what you wanted
C love eating sweet things
D a police photo of someone's face

1 __ 2 __ 3 __ 4 __

A man in Wellington, New Zealand, tried to break a shop window one night to steal some skateboarding gear. He threw a rock at the window, but it bounced off the glass and hit him on the head. The man left empty-handed. How do we know? Because the shop's CCTV camera was watching him!

In Wales, a man wanted in connection with a crime was reading the local newspaper one day when he noticed an article about him and a mugshot. The man didn't think it was a good photo, so he sent a better one to the newspaper. A week later, he was having a haircut and the police arrested him.

In Massachusetts, USA, a man with a sweet tooth was feeling hungry. There wasn't any chocolate in the house and it was the middle of the night. He couldn't wait until morning, so he smashed the glass door of his local shop, went in and took a few bars of chocolate. He also left $5!

One frosty night, two men in Leicester, England, burgled a house and then escaped by bike. Back at home an hour later, they weren't expecting a visit from the police, but that's exactly what happened. How did the police know where to go? They followed the tracks from the burglars' bikes in the frost and went straight to their house!

2 Read the article again. Choose the best heading.

A Funny British criminals
B Amusing crimes from around the world
C Crimes that the police can't solve
D Crime and vanity

3 Read the text again and circle T (true) or F (false).

1 The man in Wellington stole clothes and skateboarding equipment. **T / F**
2 The security camera in the Wellington shop was on. **T / F**
3 The police were looking for the man in Wales. **T / F**
4 The man loved the photo in the newspaper. **T / F**
5 The American man had no chocolate at home. **T / F**
6 He left the shop without paying. **T / F**
7 The men in Leicester went home on foot. **T / F**
8 The cold weather helped the police find the men. **T / F**

WORD ZONE EXTRA

Verbs of perception

4 Complete the definitions with the words in the box.

notice sense touch watch

1 ________________ : get a feeling about something
2 ________________ : look at something for a period of time
3 ________________ : put your fingers on something
4 ________________ : see and become conscious of

5 Complete the sentences with the correct form of the verbs in exercise 4.

1 He saw a strange looking man outside his house and he ________________ that something was wrong.
2 I ________________ her face and it felt very cold.
3 Did you ________________ anything unusual when you went in the room?
4 We ________________ and waited for ten minutes. Then we heard footsteps.

VOCABULARY Feelings & moods

6 Complete the adjectives.

1 I can't watch scary films. I get really f_ _ _ _ _ _ _ _ _ _.
2 Your face usually goes red when you're e_ _ _ _ _ _ _ _ _ _ _.
3 Do you cry when you watch a s_ _ film?
4 You should have a drink when you're t_ _ _ _ _ _ _.
5 My mum gets u_ _ _ _ when she hears some bad news.
6 I smile a lot when I'm h_ _ _ _.
7 Our teacher gets a_ _ _ _ if you don't do your homework.

7 Complete the sentences with the adjectives in the box.

tired calm excited hungry bored nervous annoyed

1 I'm really ________________ because it's my birthday tomorrow. I love having birthdays!
2 Emma has got an important exam today so she's feeling ________________. She couldn't eat any breakfast!
3 I'm ________________ because I did my homework last night, but I left it at home by accident.
4 They slept well because they were very ________________ after their long journey.
5 We're ________________. We haven't had breakfast this morning.
6 My mum does yoga every week. It makes her feel relaxed and ________________.
7 I didn't enjoy watching the football match. I was ________________ because I hate football.

8 Answer the questions. Write full sentences.

1 How do you feel now? Why?
____
2 How did you feel this morning? Why?
____
3 How do you feel when you are going to take a test?
____

WANT TO KNOW MORE?
Feelings and moods

9 Read the texts and try to understand the adjectives in bold. Use a dictionary if you need to.

I went to bingo with my grandma last weekend. During the first game, I was **surprised** when she stood up and shouted 'Bingo!'. Grandma went up to get her prize and I felt very **proud** of her. Then she came back looking very embarrassed. She didn't have the correct numbers. She felt really **silly**!

Maria finds it difficult to make new friends because she's very **shy**. Her best friend is Eve, but Maria is **jealous** of her right now because she's got a boyfriend, Matt. Maria likes Matt, too. Eve spends all her time with Matt so Maria feels **lonely**.

10 Match 1 – 6 with A – F to complete the sentences.

1 He felt proud when ...
2 Our neighbour felt sad and lonely when ...
3 She's bad at Maths so she was surprised when ...
4 He felt silly when ...
5 She was jealous when ...
6 She felt shy when ...

A her boyfriend asked another girl to dance.
B he came to school in his pyjamas.
C he raised £500 for charity.
D the teacher asked her to read her story to the class.
E she got four questions out of five correct in her test.
F his wife died.

1 __ 2 __ 3 __ 4 __ 5 __ 6 __

11 Answer the questions. Write full sentences.

1 When did you last feel jealous? Why?
____
2 What makes you feel proud?
____
3 What do you do when you feel lonely?
____

GRAMMAR Past continuous

1 Look at the photo. Complete the text with the past continuous form of the verbs.

chat   not come   read   relax   shine   sit   steal   wear

It was a lovely spring day yesterday. The sun [1] ________________ and it was quite warm, so John decided to go to the park. At one o'clock, he [2] ________________ on a bench in the sun. He [3] ________________ a book and [4] ________________ on his mobile. Suddenly, he heard something behind him. He turned round and saw a tall man. He [5] ________________ black shorts and a black T-shirt. He [6] ________________ to sit next to John. He [7] ________________ John's backpack! Fortunately, a lot of people [8] ________________ in the park yesterday at lunchtime and they could chase the thief.

2 What was happening in the park at one o'clock yesterday? Write the people's comments.

1 I / sunbathe

2 we / play / football

3 some children / buy / an ice cream

4 it / not rain

3 Write past continuous questions about the photo in exercise 1. Then write the correct short answers.

1 John / hold / a book?
____

2 he / eat / a sandwich?
____

3 some children / sit / next to John?
____

4 the thief / wear / sunglasses?
____

5 he / take / things out of John's bag?
____

6 it / rain?
____

4 Complete the conversation with the correct forms of the verbs in brackets.

Hayley: Guess what happened last night, Tom? It was about half past nine and Max and I [1] ________________ (sit) in the lounge.

Tom: [2] ________________ (you / watch) a film?

Hayley: No, we weren't. Max [3] ________________ (watch) Crime Watch.

Tom: Is that the programme where the public help the police to catch criminals?

Hayley: That's right. Anyway, I [4] ________________ (feel) a bit bored and I [5] ________________ (listen) to my iPod. Then, suddenly, I recognized a woman on the programme.

Tom: [6] ________________ (she / help) the police?

Hayley: No, she wasn't. She was a criminal.

Tom: No way! What [7] ________________ (she / do)?

Hayley: Well, they [8] ________________ (show) a CCTV video from a supermarket. This woman was in it. She [9] ________________ (shop), but she [10] ________________ (not put) everything in her trolley. She [11] ________________ (hide) some small things in her jacket.

Tom: You mean, she [12] ________________ (steal) things?

Hayley: That's right, and she's our neighbour!

Tom: What did you do?

Hayley: Max phoned the police and told them her name.

5 What were you and your family doing at eight o'clock this morning? Write two affirmative and two negative sentences.

1 ________________

2 ________________

3 ________________

4 ________________

LISTENING

1 Match verbs 1–5 with definitions A–E. Use a dictionary if you need to.

1 to stroll	A to run as fast as you can
2 to point at	B to walk slowly for pleasure
3 to chase	C to take someone's attention away from something
4 to sprint	D to show where something is with your finger
5 to distract	E to run after someone in order to catch them

1 __ 2 __ 3 __ 4 __ 5 __

2 17 Listen to a conversation about Sophie's trip to Barcelona. How was the trip?

A All good
B All bad
C Good and bad
D Good but a bit boring

3 17 Listen again and tick (✓) the correct box.

1 Sophie tells Oscar about Barcelona's … .	A streets	☐
	B weather and some sights	☐
	C public transport system	☐
2 Sophie sat down in the park to … .	A have lunch	☐
	B chat to some people	☐
	C have a rest	☐
3 A friendly man … .	A gave them a map	☐
	B showed them places to visit on their map	☐
	C started telling them about the Gothic Quarter	☐
4 While Sophie wasn't looking, a man … .	A ran off with her bag	☐
	B ran off with her map	☐
	C took some money out of her bag	☐
5 They chased the man … .	A but lost him in the Gothic Quarter	☐
	B and went to his house in the Gothic Quarter	☐
	C and caught him in a narrow street near the park	☐
6 The friendly man in the park … .	A was working with the thief	☐
	B was trying to steal Sophie's bag himself	☐
	C chased the thief as well	☐

TEST YOUR MEMORY!

4 Answer the questions.

1 What was the weather like on Sophie's trip?

______

2 What time was it when Sophie was sitting in the park?

______

3 How did Sophie feel when the man first started talking to her in the park?

______

4 What did Sophie shout when the man stole her bag?

______

5 How much money did Sophie have in her bag?

______

6 What else was in her bag?

______

5 Write these sentences in your language.

1 'What did you like best?' 'I'm not sure. That famous church...'

______

2 He was stealing my bag. I couldn't believe it.

______

3 'We chased him.' 'I'm impressed.'

______

READING

1 Who is the woman and what happened to her? Read the article quickly and check your answers.

A lucky escape

This is Monica Konczyk, a Polish woman in her thirties. In 2011, she was working in the UK and living in a flat opposite a furniture store in Croydon, near London. On the evening of August 8th, she smelt something burning while she was sitting in her flat. The furniture store was on fire and so was the building she lived in. When she tried to run down the stairs, thick black smoke was blocking the way. She couldn't escape, so she ran to the window at the front and shouted for help.

When professional photographer Amy Weston arrived at the scene, some people were standing in the street near the burning buildings. They kept on shouting: 'Jump!' Amy looked up and saw a woman sitting on the edge of the window. It was Monica Konczyk. Suddenly she jumped. At that moment, while Monica was falling through the air, Amy took this photo.

Fortunately, a policeman caught Monica in his arms and she wasn't injured. However, firefighters couldn't put out the fire and the furniture store burnt down. The next day, Monica's incredible story was in the headlines and Amy's dramatic photo was on the front page of the national newspapers. You need to be in the right place at the right time to be a good news photographer and have your camera ready to capture the precise moment that something dramatic happens. Amy certainly did that night.

2 Read the article again. Find words or phrases for the definitions.

1 ______________________. A shop that sells sofas, tables...
2 ______________________. Burning.
3 ______________________. Physically hurt.
4 ______________________. The main stories in the news.

3 Read the text again and circle the correct answers.

1 Monica had a ... .
A holiday in London
B job in a large shop
C job in England

2 She couldn't get out of her flat because of the ... on the stairs.
A temperature
B smoke
C people

3 The people in the street wanted Monica to ... .
A stay in the flat
B sit down
C escape from the flat

4 Amy had a ... with her when she was standing in the street.
A camera
B policeman
C a friend

5 The fire ... the shop.
A destroyed
B didn't destroy
C caused a small problem with

6 There ... interest in Monica's story the next day.
A wasn't much
B was a bit of
C was a lot of

WORD ZONE EXTRA

Phrasal verbs

4 Circle the correct words.

1 I keep **off** / **on** forgetting her name.
2 They put **out** / **away** the fire quickly.
3 Did the cinema burn **away** / **down** last year?

5 Complete the sentences with the phrasal verbs in exercise 4.

1 If the classrooms ______________________, we can't have lessons.
2 ______________________ knocking on the door. I'm sure he's in.
3 Do they use water to ______________________ a fire?

VOCABULARY People in crime

6 Complete the people in crime with the words in the box.

artist bank mug rider shop pick

1 graffiti ______________
2 ______________ger
3 joy______________
4 ______________lifter
5 ______________robber
6 ______________pocket

7 Answer the questions using the words in exercise 6.

1 Whose crime involves stealing a car?
____
2 Whose crime involves stealing things like clothes?
____
3 Whose crimes involve money?
____
4 Whose crime involves damage to buildings?
____

8 Complete the people in crime with the correct vowels.

1 h_ck_r
2 b_rgl_r
3 w_tn_ss
4 j_dg_
5 v_nd_l
6 d_t_ct_v_

9 Complete the definitions with the people in exercise 8.

1 A ______________ is a person who makes legal decisions.
2 A ______________ is a person who sees something happen.
3 A ______________ is a person involved in computer crime.
4 A ______________ is a person who tries to solve crimes.
5 A ______________ is a person who breaks into houses and steals things.
6 A ______________ is a person who maliciously destroys public or private property.

WANT TO KNOW MORE? People in crime

10 Match the people with the pictures. Which one helps the police? Use a dictionary if you need to.

arsonist blackmailer bogus caller forensic scientist kidnapper rioter

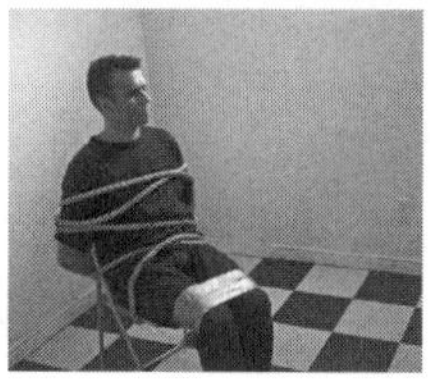

1 ______________

2 ______________

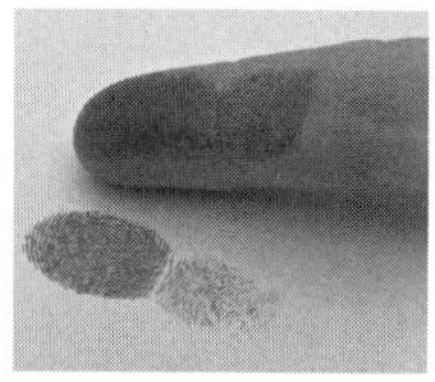

3 ______________

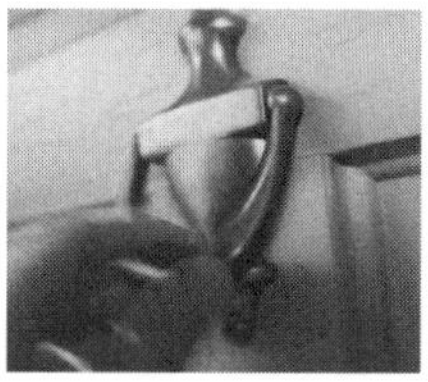

4 ______________

5 ______________

6 ______________

11 Complete the definitions with the people in exercise 10.

1 A(n) ______________ takes a person away and demands a lot of money.
2 A(n) ______________ visits homes and pretends to be a real salesman, for example. Then he steals money or possessions.
3 A(n) ______________ sets fire to a building.
4 A(n) ______________ knows something secret about you and demands money in order to keep quiet.
5 A(n) ______________ uses scientific tests to investigate crimes.
6 A(n) ______________ wants to protest about something and becomes violent in a public place.

12 Write sentences comparing some of the people in crime in exercise 10. Which criminal is the worst? Why?

____
____
____
____
____
____
____
____
____
____

GRAMMAR Past continuous & past simple | *when* & *while*

1 Write the sentences under the correct heading.

It was raining. He was giving us some homework.
We were watching a scary film. Mr Todd's mobile rang.
Some women screamed. I set off for school.

actions / situations in progress

completed actions

2 Complete the text with the correct form of the verbs in brackets.

Tonight on Crime Watch, we're asking you to help find a bogus caller. At seven o'clock yesterday evening, 85-year-old Edith Jones 1 ______________ (watch) TV when she 2 ______________ (hear) a knock at the door. It was a man in a police officer's uniform who wanted to talk about Edith's neighbour. Edith 3 ______________ (invite) him in and 4 ______________ (offer) him a cup of tea. While Edith 5 ______________ (make) his drink, the policeman 6 ______________ (stay) in the living room. But he 7 ______________ (not sit) on the sofa watching TV during that time. He 8 ______________ (look) in Edith's handbag. When he 9 ______________ (leave) the house half an hour later, he 10 ______________ (carry) £100 of Edith's money in his pocket. Edith 11 ______________ (not notice) the missing money until the next day. This is a terrible crime against an elderly lady. We must catch this bogus caller. He had short dark hair and he 12 ______________ (wear) glasses...

3 Complete the text with the correct form of the verbs in the box.

chat come drop escape give hold know rob

Banana bank robber

A man in Philadelphia, USA, 1 ______________ a banana in his pocket when he 2 ______________ a bank in September 2009. A female bank worker 3 ______________ to her colleague when the robber 4 ______________ into the bank at 9.15am. He gave her a note demanding money and said that he was carrying a gun. The frightened bank worker 5 ______________ him $800. While the robber 6 ______________ from the bank, he 7 ______________ his wallet on the floor. His ID card was in it. Detectives 8 ______________ exactly who he was!

4 Write questions about the story in exercise 3.

1 the robber / carry / a gun / when / he / rob / the bank?
____

2 what / the bank worker / do / at 9.15am?
____

3 how much money / she / give / the robber?
____

4 what / the robber / do / while / he / escape / from the bank?
____

5 how / detectives / know / the bank robber's identity?
____

5 Invent situations and complete the sentences.

1 I (meet/name of famous person) ______________ while I ______________ last summer.

2 While we (watch/ name of film) ______________ ______________ in the cinema last night, somebody ______________.

3 My dad (wear/name of item of clothing) ______________ ______________ when he ______________ ______________ to work this morning.

6 Write three sentences using *when* or *while* and the sentences from the box in exercise 1.

1 ______________________________

2 ______________________________

3 ______________________________

EXTRA CHALLENGE

Imagine that you and two friends, Ana and David, were playing a ball game near your neighbour's house at 2.15pm on Saturday afternoon. Someone broke your neighbour's window between 2.00 and 2.30pm. A police officer knows that you were playing with a ball and is asking you some questions. You need a convincing story to prove that you didn't break the window. Write answers to the questions.

What were you doing between 2.00 and 2.30 pm last Saturday?

Where exactly were you playing with the ball?

Tell me again about the ball. Can you describe it?

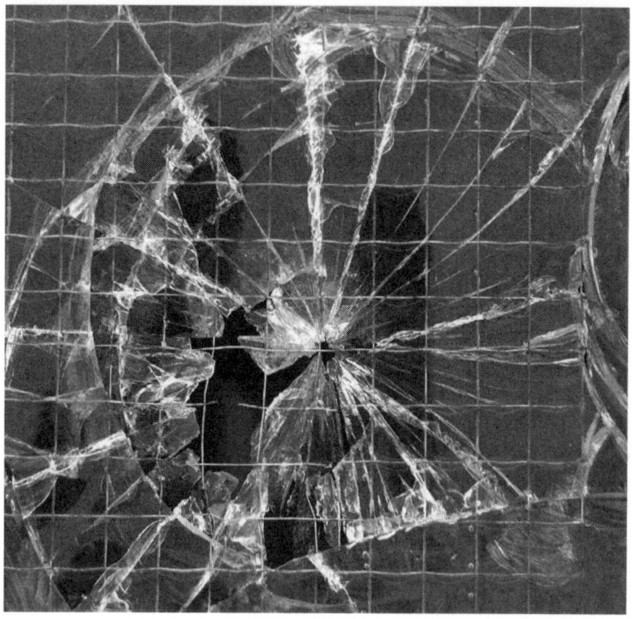

WEBQUEST

Go online and find the answers to the questions.

1 Sherlock Holmes is a famous fictional detective. Who wrote the stories?

____

2 What was Sherlock Holmes' address in London?

____

3 Who was Al Capone?

____

4 Which famous prison did he go to? For how long?

____

5 What is the acronym for the police department in New York City?

____

6 What colour are the uniforms in this police department?

____

PUZZLE

Decode the witness statement. Tick (✓) the correct burglar.

a = ❄ e = ✋ i = 💣 o = ✧ u = ⇗

1 H✋ w❄s w✋❄r💣ng ❄ h❄t.
2 H✋ w❄sn't w✋❄r💣ng gl❄ss✋s.
3 H✋ w❄s l✧✧k💣ng ⇗nh❄ppy.
4 H✋ w❄s c❄rry💣ng s✧m✋ m✧n✋y.

1 ☐

2 ☐

3 ☐

INTERACTION Talking about your weekend or holiday

1 Answer the questions. Can you remember how to express yourself?

What do you say ...

1 to ask about someone's weekend?

____

2 to find out about the other things he/she did?

____

3 to show you enjoyed yourself?

____

2 (18) Circle the correct words. Listen and check.

Zac: 1 **How / Do / Did** you have a nice day yesterday?
Milly: Yes, thanks. I had 2 **great / a great / some great** time.
Zac: What did you do?
Milly: Some friends came round and we had a barbecue.
Zac: 3 **This / That / You** sounds fun.

Marc: 4 **How / Who / What** was your trip to London?
Yolanda: Great! We went on the London Eye.
Marc: What was it 5 **love / like / hate**?
Yolanda: It was quite scary at the top!

Lola: Did you 6 **had / have / having** a good time at the football match?
Frank: No, I didn't. My team lost 9-0.
Lola: 7 **Who / What / How** awful!
Frank: And it was raining all day, so we got really wet.
Lola: 8 **That / It / What** a shame!

3 Read the dialogue and complete the summary.

Dad: Did you have a good school trip?
Jack: I had a great time in the morning, but it was boring in the afternoon.
Dad: What did you do in the morning?
Jack: We went to the British Museum.
Dad: What was it like?
Jack: It was brilliant. We saw some Ancient Egyptian mummies.
Dad: That sounds fun. What else did you see?
Jack: The oldest human-made object in the museum. It's 1.8 million years old!
Dad: Amazing! How about the afternoon? Why was it boring?
Jack: Because we went to Oxford Street.
Dad: What did you do there?
Jack: Shopping! And I hate shopping!
Dad: I know!
Jack: And then someone stole Gina's purse at the underground station. Poor Gina! It ruined the day for her.
Dad: What a shame!

1 __________ went on a 2 __________ yesterday. He enjoyed the 3 __________ when they visited the 4 __________. He didn't enjoy the 5 __________ because they went 6 __________ on 7 __________. His dad shows sympathy when he finds out that 8 __________ was a victim of crime.

4 Complete the dialogue.

You: (Ask about Elsa's holiday.)
1 ____________________________
Elsa: I had a great time in Florida. We went to Universal Studios in Orlando.
You: (React positively and ask about the other things she did.)
2 ____________________________
Elsa: We relaxed on the beach and we went swimming.
You: (Find out what the weather was like.)
3 ____________________________
Elsa: It was quite cold and I lost my watch in the sea.
You: (Show sympathy with Elsa.)
4 ____________________________
Elsa: Anyway, how about you? How was your holiday?
You: (Respond negatively.)
5 ____________________________

YOUR TURN TO SPEAK

5 (19) Revise the *Express yourself* box on page 68 of the Student's Book. Then listen to the people and respond.

WRITING A story

WRITING SKILL Past time expression

1 Complete the sentences with the correct form of the verbs in brackets. Use the past continuous or past simple.

1 Just then, Jasper ________________ (run) into the kitchen and ________________ (start) barking.
2 Then, I ________________ (walk) into the hall and ________________ (open) the front door.
3 Last Saturday, it ________________ (be) the first day of the summer holidays.
4 Suddenly, the boy ________________ (put) down my things, ________________ (kick) poor Jasper and ________________ (escape).
5 I ________________ (read) a magazine in the garden when I ________________ (hear) a knock at the door.

2 Complete the text with the sentences in exercise 1.

A frightened burglar

by Clara Bone

1 ________________ ________________.
The sun was shining and it was a beautiful day. I was feeling really happy. I didn't have school for six weeks! My parents were working and my brother was playing tennis. It was just me and our dog, Jasper, at home. 2 ________________.
I got up and went into the house. 3 ________________ ________________. A young woman was standing there. Jasper was very excited and the woman started playing with him immediately. She was very friendly and she explained that she was trying to find her friend's house, but she was lost. She told me the address and I started giving her directions.
4 ________________.
I ran after him and I couldn't believe my eyes. A teenage boy was standing near the back door and he was holding my mp3 player and laptop. He was trying to get out of the house, but Jasper was blocking the way. He was barking loudly and jumping up and down. The boy was really frightened.
5 ________________.
I ran after him, but he was sprinting down the road and he wasn't alone. The young woman was with him. I realized that they were working together. While the woman was distracting me, the boy was stealing my things. Fortunately for me, he was scared of dogs!

3 Read the text again and answer the questions.

1 When did the attempted burglary take place?
____
2 What did Clara do when she heard a knock at the door?
____
3 What did the woman want Clara to do?
____
4 How did Clara discover the burglar?
____
5 Why couldn't the burglar leave the house?
____
6 How did he escape in the end?
____

4 Look at the *Writing Reference* on page 118. Then write a story about a frightening day last summer. Invent the details if necessary. Write about:

– the place
– the background
– description
– the people
– the events

Reminder

- Check your past continuous and past simple forms.
- Check your past time expressions.

____
____
____
____
____
____
____
____
____
____
____
____
____
____
____
____
____
____
____
____

Review Units 4-6

VOCABULARY

1 Complete the word groups with the words in the box.

around plain shallow ship thirsty vandal

1 valley mountain lake ________
2 lorry tram train ________
3 hungry nervous tired ________
4 burglar mugger pickpocket ________
5 through across between ________
6 wide heavy long ________

2 Write the opposites.

1 empty f________
2 ugly b________
3 safe d________
4 up d________
5 over u________
6 away from t________
7 happy s________
8 nervous c________

3 Complete the sentences with the words in the box.

along bored coach desert popular witness

1 The driest place in the world is a ________.
2 It takes two hours to travel by ________ to London.
3 The ________ described the bank robber to the police.
4 That café is very ________ with teenagers.
5 We were walking ________ the road when we saw Joe.
6 I was ________ so I started reading a book.

GRAMMAR

4 Complete the text with the verbs in the box. Use the past simple or past continuous form.

not be decide go leave not rain shine take not want

Last July I [1] ________ on holiday to Sicily with my parents. One day, my dad and I [2] ________ to climb Mount Etna. My mum [3] ________ to do it, so she stayed in Catania. The sun [4] ________ when Dad and I [5] ________ the hotel, but the weather changed quickly. It [6] ________ when we got to the top, but it was cold and cloudy. Unfortunately, the views [7] ________ very good, so I only [8] ________ two photos!

5 Complete the questions with the past simple or past continuous form of the verbs. Then answer the questions.

1 ________ (you / do) your homework yesterday?
(✓) ________
2 ________ (your parents / sleep) at 9pm last night?
(✗) ________
3 ________ (it / rain) when you woke up this morning?
(✓) ________
4 ________ (your friend / have) a party last Saturday?
(✗) ________

6 Complete the sentences with the adjectives. Use the comparative or superlative form, or the adjective as it is.

1 Milk is the ________ drink in the world. (good)
2 My feet are ________ than your feet. (big)
3 I think English is ________ than French. (easy)
4 She can't run as ________ as me. (far)

REVIEW CHECK

7 Read the text and choose the correct words.

Mount Etna is in the north-east of the Italian island of Sicily in the Mediterranean [1]... . It is [2] ... volcano in Europe and it is one of [3] ... active volcanoes in the world. Mount Vesuvius is another of Italy's volcanoes, but Etna is three times [4] ... than Vesuvius.

The first eruption at Mount Etna [5] ... place about half a million years ago, but its most powerful eruption [6] ... in 1669. Lava [7] ... down the mountain and reached the town of Catania, almost 16 km away.

More recently, Mount Etna [8] ... erupting on the night of 9th February 2012 while I [9] ... in Catania. I [10] ... frightened when it happened. I took lots of photos!

1		
A River	**B** Stream	**C** Sea
2		
A larger	**B** largest	**C** the largest
3		
A most	**B** the most	**C** more
4		
A higher	**B** the higher	**C** highest
5		
A was taking	**B** taked	**C** took
6		
A is	**B** was	**C** were
7		
A travelled	**B** did travel	**C** was travelling
8		
A start	**B** started	**C** was starting
9		
A was staying	**B** were staying	**C** stayed
10		
A not felt	**B** didn't feel	**C** don't feel

Video

NASA

BEFORE YOU WATCH

1 Read the introduction and the questions in NOW WATCH.

Introduction

NASA stands for 'National Aeronautics and Space Administration'. NASA is the United States government agency that is responsible for the nation's civilian space program and for aeronautics and aerospace research.

NOW WATCH

2 Answer the questions.

1 When did NASA come into existence?

______

2 What were the Soviet Union's achievements in the Space Race? And what about the US?

______

3 Why was the Apollo-Soyuz Test Project important?

______

4 Apart from amazing pictures of space, what achievement of the Hubble Space Telescope is mentioned?

______

5 Name two types of research that NASA is doing on Earth.

______

FOLLOW UP

3 Go online and find out about NASA. Write an interesting fact to share with your class.

Did you know that...?

______

7 You've got a friend

READING

1 Read the texts quickly. Match the words and the definitions.

1 set
2 dormitory
3 platform
4 luggage trolley
5 broomstick

A you get on and off trains here
B in stories about magic, you travel through the air on this
C you sleep here at a boarding school
D the scenery for a film or play
E you carry your bags on this in a station or airport

1_ 2_ 3_ 4_ 5_

Chloe, 13
I've been on the Harry Potter Studio Tour in London. If you're crazy about Harry Potter, you should definitely go on it. You visit some of the sets, such as the boys' dormitory where Harry and Ron slept, and a classroom where they practised magic. It's fantastic. I've walked along Diagon Alley and touched Hagrid's motorcycle!
∧ | ∨ Reply Share

Jack, 12
Have you been to Platform 9¾ at Kings Cross Station in London? We have! We've seen all the Harry Potter films and we love it when the students go through the wall onto Platform 9¾. There's a sign on the wall at Kings Cross that says Platform 9¾ and there's a luggage trolley in the wall. A friend took a photo of me holding on to it!
∧ | ∨ Reply Share

Lucy, 14
I've watched the first seven Harry Potter films without stopping! I started at 2.30pm and finished at 8 o'clock the next morning. I did it before they released the final Harry Potter film. I wanted to see all the films again before I saw that.
∧ | ∨ Reply Share

Isabel, 15
My brother Xavi plays Quidditch at his school, the sport Harry Potter plays. Well, it's a version of Quidditch because obviously we can't fly like Harry and Ron can on their broomsticks! Xavi has Quidditch practice once a week. I've watched one of his matches. It's fast and exciting. The ball is called the 'quaffle' like in the books.
∧ | ∨ Reply Share

2 Read the texts again. Circle the correct words.

The texts are [1] **stories / postcards / messages** on [2] **a noticeboard / a webpage / an advert**. They are about people's [3] **opinions / experiences / favourite parts** of [4] **Harry Potter / the Harry Potter actors / the Harry Potter films**.

3 Read the texts again and complete the sentences. Write *Chloe*, *Jack*, *Lucy*, *Xavi* or *Nobody*.

1 __________ has stayed awake all night.
2 __________ has seen some of the objects they used in the films.
3 __________ has walked through the wall onto Platform 9 ¾.
4 __________ has thrown a quaffle.
5 __________ has taken a picture at a London station.
6 __________ has flown on a broomstick.
7 __________ has visited the place where they made the Harry Potter films.
8 __________ has slept in Harry and Ron's dormitory.

WORD ZONE EXTRA

***practise* or *practice*?**

4 Find *practise* and *practice* in the texts. Then complete the definitions with the words.

1 __________, *n.*
A period of doing an activity in order to become good at it.
2 __________, *vb.*
To do an activity often so that you become good at it.

5 Complete the sentences with *practice* or *practise*.

1 Have you got football __________ tonight?
2 You should __________ the piano every day.
3 Let's __________ irregular verbs today.
4 With __________, our English is getting better.

VOCABULARY Skills & interests

6 Complete the text with the prepositions in the box.

about at in into of on

Matthew Lewis is an actor. He played Neville Longbottom in the Harry Potter films. He's keen [1] ________________ football and supports Leeds United. He's interested [2] ________________ computer games, especially football ones. He's also [3] ________________ music. He likes singing, but he's terrible [4] ________________ it! He's crazy [5] ________________ the band Oasis. Matthew is fond [6] ________________ the number 11 because he was 11 when started acting in the Harry Potter films. He has a tattoo of the number on his right arm.

LAST NAME:	Lewis	**DATE OF BIRTH:**	27th June 1989
FIRST NAME:	Matthew	**PLACE OF BIRTH:**	Leeds, England

7 Rewrite the sentences so that they mean the same.

1 I really hate heavy metal music.
I can't ________________ .
2 You're terrible at playing tennis.
You aren't very ________________ .
3 Rock music is OK.
I don't ________________ .
4 They adore watching TV.
They really ________________ .
5 I don't really like animals.
I'm not very ________________ .

8 Write about a family member's skills and interests. Use different expressions from exercises 6 and 7.

____

WANT TO KNOW MORE? Adjectives + prepositions

9 Read the text. Then complete the sentences with the adjectives and prepositions in bold. Use a dictionary if you need to.

Manchester in England is **famous for** its two football teams - Manchester United and Manchester City. Both teams are **brilliant at** football. My dad is a big fan of Manchester City and my mum supports Manchester United. Sometimes I'm **fed up with** the things they say about each other's teams, such as 'I can't stand your number 9'. Right now, my dad is very **proud of** Manchester City. They've won the league. Their supporters are very **excited about** it because they haven't won it for a long time. Who did they beat? You probably aren't **surprised at** the fact that it was Manchester United!

1 When something unusual happens, you're usually ________________ it.
2 When a friend of yours does something very good, you're ________________ him / her.
3 When everyone knows who you are, you're ________________ something.
4 When you're very good at something, you're ________________ it.
5 When you're bored with something, you're ________________ it.
6 When you're really happy about something, you're ________________ it.

10 Complete the sentences with the words in the box.

at scoring goals at the price
about it for them of her with it

1 Suzy has passed her exam. We're really proud ________________ .
2 He plays for Manchester City. He's brilliant ________________ .
3 London has got some great shops. It's famous ________________ .
4 It's your party tomorrow. We're excited ________________ .
5 The weather is awful. I'm fed up ________________ .
6 The tickets cost £200. We were surprised ________________ .

11 Answer the questions. Write full sentences.

1 What is your town / region famous for?
____
2 What are you especially proud of? Why?
____
3 What are you fed up with? Why?
____

GRAMMAR Present perfect: *ever* & *never*

1 Complete the sentences with the present perfect of the verbs in brackets.

Edna, 85

1 Edna ________________ (have) a happy life.
2 She ________________ (live) in the same town.
3 She ________________ (not travel) much.
4 Edna and her husband ________________ (visit) London.
5 They ________________ (see) the Queen a few times.
6 They ________________ (not speak) to her.
7 Edna ________________ (write) lots of emails in her life.
8 She ________________ (not send) a text message.

Edna's grandson, Bruno, 24

9 Bruno ________________ (study) at university.
10 He ________________ (go) to lots of different countries.
11 He ________________ (not stay) in his hometown.
12 Bruno and some friends ________________ (trek) through a rainforest.
13 They ________________ (kayak) along the River Amazon.
14 They ____________________________ (not swim) in it.
15 Bruno ____________________________ (drink) mate in South America.
16 He ____________________________ (eat) tamales.

2 Complete the sentences with the correct form of the pairs of verbs in the box. Use the present perfect.

have / never be	play / never win	ride / never fall	see / not read	not visit / try

1 I ____________________________ tennis, but I ____________________________ a match.
2 They ____________________________ Japan, but they ____________________________ sushi.
3 We ____________________________ the Harry Potter films, but we ____________________________ the books.
4 My sister ____________________________ a boyfriend, but she ____________________________ in love.
5 I ____________________________ a bike, but I ____________________________ off one.

3 Write questions with the present perfect and *ever*. Then write true short answers.

1 you / act / in a film?
____
2 your English teacher / arrive / late?
____
3 you and your best friend / have / an argument?
____
4 it / snow / in your country in summer?
____
5 your parents / study / another language?
____
6 you / stay / awake all night?
____

4 Complete the exchanges with the correct form of the verbs in brackets. Use the present perfect.

Rani: [1] ____________________________ (your parents / ever / fly) in a helicopter?
Lucas: No, they haven't, but they [2] ________________ (travel) in a hot air balloon.
Rani: Really?
Lucas: Yes, they did it last year for my dad's 40th birthday. He adored it, but my mum didn't!

Fred: [3] ________________________ (you / ever / see) a koala?
Lara: Yes, I have. I [4] ____________________________ (hold) one in my arms, too.
Fred: No way!
Lara: Yes, I went to a zoo in Sydney when I was in Australia three years ago.

Suzy: [5] ____________________________ (your brother / ever / run) a marathon?
Tim: No, he hasn't, but he [6] ____________________ (take) part in a 10 km race.
Suzy: Really?
Tim: Yes, it was last month. He didn't win it, but he came 4th!

5 Think about you and one of your grandparents. Write a paragraph about your different experiences.

____
____
____
____
____
____
____

LISTENING

1 Complete the poster with the words in the box. Use a dictionary if you need to.

audience   auditions   judges   perform   talent show

Are You A Star?

Everyone's favourite [1] ______________ is in Cardiff on **27TH OCTOBER**.

Are you keen on singing? Are you into dancing? Do you love playing an instrument?

Come and [2] ______________ at the Cardiff Arena in front of our four famous [3] ______________!

Doors are open at 9am and [4] ______________ for the show start at 10am.

Terrible at performing?

It doesn't matter!

Come and be part of the [5] ______________.

TICKETS ARE FREE!

2 (20) Listen to an audition at the talent show and complete the table.

Name of act	
Number of people	
Type of song	

3 (20) Listen again and decide if the sentences are true (T) or false (F).

1 Mario is younger than Melissa. T / F
2 It's the first time Melissa has performed in front of an audience. T / F
3 Mario and Melissa didn't plan to go on a talent show. T / F
4 They met each other on the first day of primary school. T / F
5 At first, they didn't enjoy listening to the same music. T / F
6 Mario has never had singing lessons. T / F

TEST YOUR MEMORY!

4 Answer the questions.

1 Where are Mario and Melissa from?
____
2 How does Melissa feel at the beginning of the audition?
____
3 How long have Mario and Melissa sung together?
____
4 What sort of music did Melissa love when Mario first met her?
____
5 Where did they go and see a musical?
____
6 Which musical is their song from?
____

5 Write these sentences in your language.

1 'We're both 14.' 'Actually, I'm 15.'
____
2 Believe it or not, it was our Maths teacher!
____
3 I dropped all my books. It was a nightmare!
____

READING

1 Look at the photo. What relationship do you think the girls have with each other? Read the text quickly and check your answer.

The spitting image of me

Katy and Joanna were born on the same day in August 1994 and grew up like sisters. They played together a lot, went to the same primary school and sat next to each other in class. They were inseparable. They also looked like each other. In fact, Katy said when she looked at Joanna, it was like looking at herself in a mirror!

When Joanna was eight, her dad got a job in South Africa, so she and her family went to live in Cape Town. The girls were very upset and promised to keep in touch. At first, they wrote to each other every week. Then, as Joanna settled into her new life and made new friends, she stopped writing as often. After a year, the girls completely lost touch with each other.

Ten years later, Katy was tidying her room when she found an old photo of the two of them when they were young. Suddenly, she really wanted to see Joanna again. She went online and found a website that reunites people. Three days later, she got a message from Joanna. She was living in London again.

The girls have met since then and discovered a lot of coincidences. They've both been vegetarians for several years. They've both dyed their hair red. They're both into English Literature and they have the same favourite book! The girls really enjoyed themselves when they met. They've promised to keep in touch forever.

2 Look at the title of the text. What does it mean?

A someone who looks completely different from you
B someone who looks a bit like you
C someone who looks exactly like you

3 Read the text again and tick (✓) YES or NO.

		YES	NO
1	Katy and Joanna are the same age.	☐	☐
2	They spent a little time together when they were very young.	☐	☐
3	Joanna's family moved to another country.	☐	☐
4	The girls have stayed in contact since that time.	☐	☐
5	Katy found a picture of Joanna on the internet.	☐	☐
6	The girls have stopped eating meat.	☐	☐
7	They share some of the same interests.	☐	☐
8	They don't want to be friends anymore.	☐	☐

EXTRA WORD ZONE

Reflexive pronouns

4 Complete the table with words from the text.

singular	plural
myself	ourselves
yourself	yourselves
himself 1 ____________ itself	2 ____________

5 Complete the sentences with the correct reflexive pronoun.

1 I fell over and hurt ____________ last night.
2 Robin has never had piano lessons. He's taught ____________ to play.
3 'Did you enjoy ____________ at the party?' 'No, we didn't like the music.'
4 My sister loves looking at ____________ in the mirror.

VOCABULARY Describing people

6 Do the crossword.

Across

3 The hair between a man's nose and mouth.
5 Small brown spots on your skin.
6 Having no hair.

Down

1 You wear these to see better.
2 You can have this in your ear or your nose.
4 The hair on a man's chin.

7 Complete the sentences with the opposites.

1 My hair isn't long. It's s _ _ _ t.
2 He's got curly hair. It isn't s _ _ _ _ _ _ _ t.
3 You aren't short. You're very t _ _ l.
4 I'm w _ _ l-b _ _ _ t. I'm not thin.
5 Her hair isn't black or brown. It's f _ _ r.
6 She isn't tall or short. She's m _ _ _ _ m h _ _ _ _ t.
7 I'm not slim. I'm p _ _ _ p.
8 He's never cheerful. He's always s _ _ _ _ _ s.

8 Write a description of yourself.

____
____
____
____
____
____
____
____
____
____

WANT TO KNOW MORE?
Parts of the face

9 Label the picture. Use a dictionary if you need to.

cheeks chin eyebrows eyelashes
forehead lips nose teeth

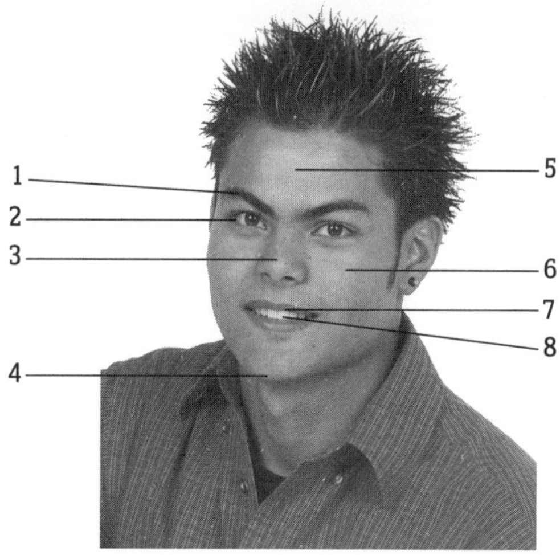

10 Look at the adjectives and nouns. Circle the adjective that you can't use.

1 a **wide / narrow / clever** forehead
2 **plump / bushy / thin** eyebrows
3 a **long / curly / big** nose
4 **straight / wavy / white** teeth
5 **short / thin / plump** lips
6 **long / thick / tall** eyelashes
7 a **pointed / bald / rounded** chin
8 **plump / high / straight** cheeks

11 Continue the description of yourself in exercise 8. Use the nouns and adjectives in exercises 9 and 10.

____
____
____
____
____
____
____
____
____
____

GRAMMAR Present perfect: *How long*, *for* & *since* | *been* & *gone*

1 Write *for* or *since*.

1 __________ September
2 __________ two minutes
3 __________ a decade
4 __________ Monday
5 __________ 1998
6 __________ ten months
7 __________ a long time
8 __________ Christmas
9 __________ 7 o'clock this morning
10 __________ years

2 Complete the exchanges with the correct form of the verbs in the box and *for* and *since*.

be not eat live not see support wear

1 **Tom:** You wear glasses.
Chris: I know! I 1 ______________ ______________ them 2 ______________ March.
2 **Bill:** Are you hungry?
Joe: I'm starving. I 3 ______________ ______________ anything 4 ______________ hours.
3 **Ben:** Is your dad keen on football?
Martin: Yes. He 5 ______________ Chelsea 6 ______________ he was young.
4 **Carla:** Jenny? It's me, Carla.
Jenny: Carla! We 7 ______________ each other 8 ______________ over 20 years.
5 **Cody:** Why are you tired?
David: I 9 ______________ awake 10 ______________ two o'clock this morning!
6 **Jane:** Did you grow up in this house?
Cathy: Yes, I did. My parents 11 ______________ here 12 ______________ 1988.

3 Write the questions with *How long* then write true answers.

1 you / be / at this school
______________________________________?
____
2 you / live / in this town
______________________________________?
____
3 you / have / the shoes that you're wearing
______________________________________?
____
4 you and the person next to you / know / each other
______________________________________?
____

4 Complete the dialogue with *been* or *gone*.

Linda: You look well.
Shirley: Thanks. I've 1 ______________ to Majorca for a week.
Linda: Really? Was it your first visit?
Shirley: No. I've 2 ______________ there a few times. By the way, where's Emma?
Linda: She's 3 ______________ shopping. She's still there. There's a new shop in town. Have you 4 ______________ to it?
Shirley: No, I haven't. Has Emma 5 ______________ to town on her own?
Linda: No, Maria has 6 ______________ with her.

5 Complete the dialogue with the correct present perfect form of the verbs in brackets and *for* and *since*.

Joe: Who's your hero?
Alice: David Beckham. I 1 ______________ (admire) him 2 ______________ I was young.
Joe: I know he 3 ______________ (be) a fantastic footballer 4 ______________ years and he 5 ______________ (score) loads of goals, but I don't know much else about him. For example, how long 6 ______________ (he / be) married?
Alice: 7 ______________ 1999. His wife, Victoria, was a pop singer, but she 8 ______________ (not sing) in public for over 5 years.
Joe: 9 ______________ (David / ever / live) abroad?
Alice: Yes, he 10 ______________ (live) in Italy and Spain.
Joe: What numbers 11 ______________ (he / wear) on his football shirts?
Alice: He 12 ______________ (wear) two numbers – number 7 and number 23.
Joe: Wow! You *are* a big fan of Beckham. 13 ______________ (you / ever / meet) him?
Alice: No, I 14 ______________ (never / meet) him, but I'm one of his followers on Twitter. I 15 ______________ (not write) a message 16 ______________ yesterday, so I think I'll write something now.

EXTRA CHALLENGE

Imagine you are interviewing someone who has travelled a lot and done some interesting things. Write six *Have you ever ...?* questions to find out about their experiences. Use the verbs in the box and the photos to help you.

eat climb hold play ride run
see smell taste touch visit walk

	QUESTIONS	YES / NO	MORE INFORMATION
1			
2			
3			
4			
5			
6			

Now invent their answers. When the answer is 'yes', invent more information about their experience. Be imaginative!

WEBQUEST

Go online and find the answers to the questions.

1 Who wrote the Harry Potter books? How many Harry Potter books has she written?

______

2 What's the title of the fifth Harry Potter book?

______

3 How many people went to the first Glastonbury Festival in 1970? How much was a ticket?

______

4 How many people went to the Glastonbury Festival in 2011? How much was a ticket?

______

5 Where exactly is Madame Tussauds in London?

______

6 Outside the UK, which other cities in Europe have a Madame Tussauds tourist attraction?

______

PUZZLE

Put the words with the same font together in order to make questions. Then write true answers.

done	in	slept	*on*
floor	*appeared*	extreme	school
an	the	play	on
TV	a	sport	acted

1 Have you ever ______ ?

______

2 *Have you ever* ______ ?

______

3 Have you ever ______ ?

______

4 Have you ever ______ ?

______

INTERACTION Apologizing and accepting apologies

1 Answer the questions. Can you remember how to express yourself?

What do you say ...

1 to apologize for being late?

____

2 to accept an apology for being late?

____

3 to apologize for breaking a window?

____

4 to respond to someone's apology for breaking a window? (You're upset.)

____

2 (21) Complete the exchanges with the correct words. Listen and check.

Alice: Have you got my pen?
Sam: 1 __________ afraid I've broken it. I'm really sorry.
Alice: It's 2 __________ a problem. It was only a cheap one.

Sarah: I'm sorry 3 __________ I've forgotten your name.
Zac: It's Zac.
Sarah: I'm so sorry. I can never remember names.
Zac: It's 4 __________ right. Don't feel bad 5 __________ it.

Helen: I've lost that book you lent me.
Fred: 6 __________ no! How did you do 7 __________?
Helen: I was reading it on the bus and now I haven't got it. I'm sorry.
Fred: 8 __________ worry. It's not a problem.

3 Read the dialogue and circle T (true) or F (false).

Teacher: You're late, Martin.
Martin: I'm really sorry, Miss.
Teacher: You've been late every day this week, Martin. What's the problem?
Martin: I can't wake up in the morning.
Teacher: Then use an alarm clock.
Martin: I'm afraid I've broken my alarm clock.
Teacher: What about the alarm on your mobile?
Martin: I've lost my mobile, Miss.
Teacher: Oh dear! It's not your lucky day, is it, Martin? Have you got your homework?
Martin: Yes, Miss. Here it is.
Teacher: Oh, no! This book is wet.
Martin: I'm sorry, Miss.
Teacher: How did that happen?
Martin: I was running to school when I dropped my book in a puddle. I'm so sorry.
Teacher: It's OK, Martin. We can dry it.

1 Martin hasn't been late recently. T / F
2 His alarm clock doesn't work. T / F
3 He's never had a mobile phone. T / F
4 Martin hasn't done his homework. T / F
5 He fell in a puddle on the way to school. T / F
6 His teacher accepts his apology. T / F

4 Complete the dialogue.

Elsa: I can't send any texts.
You: (Respond.)
1 ______________________
Elsa: I've broken the screen on my phone.
You: (Find out what happened.)
2 ______________________
Elsa: It was on my bedroom floor when I stepped on it. Have you got a phone you can lend me?
You: (Apologize and say that you haven't.)
3 ______________________
Elsa: OK.
You: (Apologize again more strongly.)
4 ______________________
Elsa: It's OK. Don't feel bad about it.

YOUR TURN TO SPEAK

5 (22) Revise the *Express yourself* box on page 80 of the Student's Book. Then listen to the people and respond.

WRITING An essay

WRITING SKILL Referencing words

1 Replace the words in bold with a referencing word. Circle the correct words.

1 She wants to study medicine **at Bristol University**.
A their B that C there
2 Our parents love listening to **Claudia and me**.
A them B her C us
3 **Her nose** is the thing she hates most about herself.
A That B There C He
4 She's played **tennis** since she was four.
A him B her C it
5 Everyone wants to be friends with **Claudia**.
A him B her C it
6 **Being a good listener and helping me** are the qualities I like best in her.
A That B Those C Them
7 She also plays games with **the elderly people**.
A them B these C those

2 Complete the text with the sentences in exercise 1. Use the referencing words.

A special person

I really admire my older sister, Claudia. She's always cheerful. She likes making jokes and she smiles a lot. 1 ______________________________. She's got long fair hair and beautiful blue eyes. She thinks she's got a big nose, but she hasn't. 2 ______________________________.
Claudia is very clever and wants to be a doctor when she's older. She's visited Bristol University. 3 ______________________________. Claudia studies a lot, but she also finds time to help others. She works as a volunteer at a home for the elderly. She's done it for two years. She chats to the elderly people. 4 ______________________________.
Claudia is also into sport and she's brilliant at tennis. 5 ______________________________.
She's played in three competitions this year and she's won two of them. I prefer music to sport and I adore singing. Claudia plays the piano and we often do duets. 6 ______________________________. They think we should make an album!
Claudia is a loyal sister. She's a good listener and always helps me when I've got a problem. 7 ______________________________.

3 Read the text again and choose the correct answers.

1 The writer is **older than / younger than / the same age as** Claudia.
2 Claudia makes people **laugh / cry / study**.
3 She **has studied / hasn't studied / is studying** at university.
4 She **can't stand / is fond of / doesn't like** elderly people.
5 She is **crazy about / is terrible at / isn't keen on** sport.
6 The writer **wants to share / doesn't share / shares an** interest with Claudia.

4 Look at the Writing Reference on page 119. Then write a text about a special person. Write about:

– their appearance
– their personality
– their experiences
– their achievements
– the qualities you like best in this person

Reminder
- *Check your present perfect forms and for and since.*
- *Check your referencing words.*

____
____
____
____
____
____
____
____
____
____
____
____
____
____
____
____
____
____
____
____

8 Nice work

READING

1 **Read the job adverts. How many of the jobs are indoors?**

2 **Complete the adverts with the sentences below.**

A You have to go out whatever the weather.
B You must enjoy speaking on the phone.
C You don't have to do any housework.
D You must be friendly and presentable.

SITUATIONS VACANT

SHOP ASSISTANT WANTED

A teenage boy or girl (must be over 16) to work on Saturdays in a busy coffee shop. Duties include making sandwiches and serving customers. [1] ______________. Long hair must be in a ponytail at all times. Uniform provided. £5.50 an hour.

Paper boy/girl

Teenager (over 14) needed to deliver newspapers for local newsagent's. Six days a week. Must be at the shop at 6.30am. The paper round takes 30 minutes. You need to be fit, energetic and reliable.
2 ______________.
£20/week.
N.B.: You must have a bike.

Teatime girl

I am a mum with a schoolchild, a toddler, a baby and two dogs. I need someone (over 14) to help me from 4.00pm till 6.00pm three days a week. You need to do fun things with the older kids like playing games or drawing and painting.
3 ______________. Monday, Wednesday and Friday, but can change days if necessary. £5 / hour.

CALL CENTRE OPERATOR

We sell beauty products by mail order and we need students (16 and over) to work in our call centre at weekends. No experience necessary, but good communication skills are essential.
4 ______________. No personal calls while you're working. Good rates of pay.

3 **These teenagers want to earn some money. Choose the best job from the adverts in exercise 2 for them.**

1 Jack is very sporty and loves doing exercise. He's happiest when he's outside. He's a very confident person and gets on well with lots of different people, especially children.

Best job: ______________

2 Leah is very creative and a brilliant artist. She's got a good sense of humour and is fun to be with. However, she's very shy with people she's never met before. She's bad at cooking and hates cycling.

Best job: ______________

3 Luke is a good communicator and he's brilliant at selling things. However, he's an untidy person and never helps around the house. He finds it difficult get up in the mornings. He's allergic to dogs.

Best job: ______________

4 Teresa is a talented netball player and plays on the school team. She has netball practice after school twice a week. She's very sociable and wants a job where she meets people. She enjoys housework.

Best job: ______________

EXTRA WORD ZONE

Compound nouns

4 **Match words from A and B to make compound nouns. Are they one word or two separate words?**

A	B
beauty coffee house netball paper school	child player products round shop work

1 ______________ 4 ______________
2 ______________ 5 ______________
3 ______________ 6 ______________

5 **Write two true sentences for you using some of the compound nouns in exercise 4.**

1 ______________
____

2 ______________
____

VOCABULARY Jobs

6 Complete the jobs with the correct vowels.

1 d__ct__r
2 f__r__f__ght__r
3 v__t
4 p__l__t
5 __rch__t__ct
6 sh__p __ss__st__nt
7 p__l__c__ __ff__c__r
8 b__s dr__v__r
9 f__rm__r
10 n__rs__
11 b__ __ld__r
12 s__l__s r__pr__s__nt__t__v__

7 Write the jobs in exercise 6 under the correct heading.

Animals

Medicine

Sales and shops

Emergency services

Transport

Construction

8 Write about a family member's job. Explain exactly what he / she does and give your opinion of his / her job.

____
____
____
____
____

WANT TO KNOW MORE?
Jobs

9 Match the jobs with the things associated with them. Use a dictionary if you need to.

cook flight attendant hairdresser journalist librarian miner pharmacist

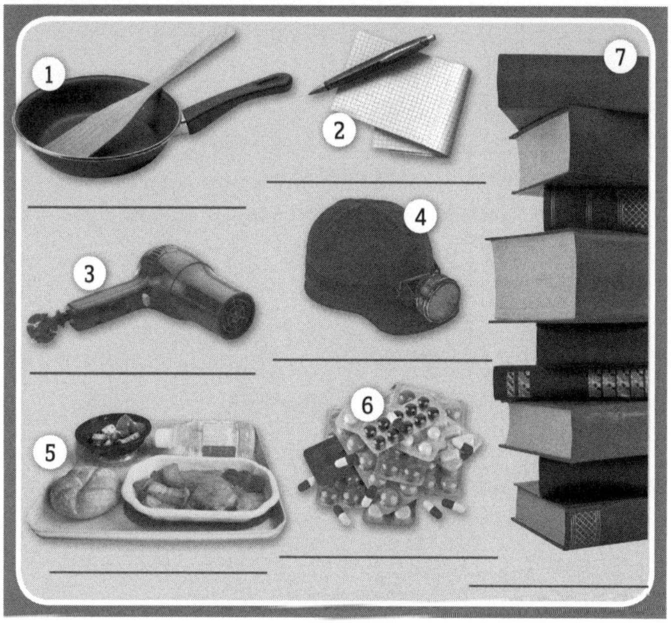

10 Whose comments are these? Write the names of the jobs in exercise 9.

1 *I'm interested in current affairs.* journalist
2 *Travelling by air is exciting.* ____________
3 *I don't mind being underground.* ____________
4 *Food is the best thing in the world.* ____________
5 *I'm crazy about reading.* ____________
6 *I like helping sick people get well.* ____________
7 *I' love making people look good.* ____________

11 Choose two of the jobs in exercise 9 and complete the sentences with your own ideas.

1 Being a ____________ can be exciting because you ____________
____________.

2 Being a ____________ can be boring because you ____________
____________.

GRAMMAR Modals: rules & obligations

1 Complete the text with *must* or *mustn't*.

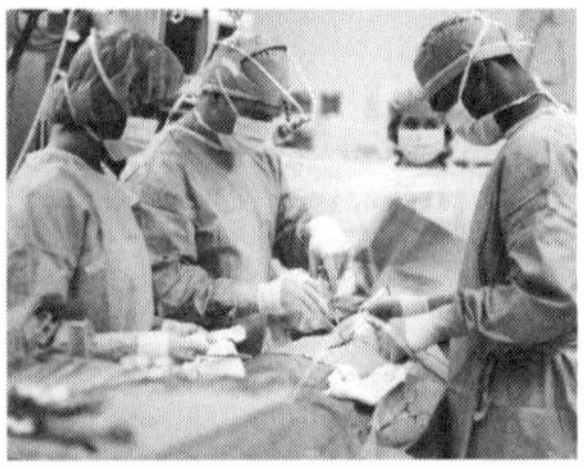

James is a surgeon. You [1] ______ become a doctor before you can train to be a surgeon. When James is operating, he and his colleagues [2] ______ wear special clothes and shoes. Before an operation, they [3] ______ wash their hands well. After that, they [4] ______ touch anything that isn't sterile. Being a surgeon is well-paid, but it's also stressful. James [5] ______ lose concentration during an operation and he [6] ______ panic if there is a problem. He [7] ______ also be very careful. He [8] ______ leave anything in the patient!

2 Complete the sentences with *mustn't*, *have to* or *don't have to* and the verbs in the box.

answer be carry go ignore leave

It's Saturday today, so James [1] ______ to the hospital. He's playing tennis with some friends in the local park right now. Anyone can play there. You [2] ______ a member of a tennis club. James can't completely forget about work during the weekend. He [3] ______ a mobile phone with him at all times. He [4] ______ it at home! He [5] ______ the mobile when he hears it. He [6] ______ the phone call as quickly as possible to find out what the emergency is.

3 Write true sentences about you with *mustn't*, *have to* or *don't have to*.

1 I / make my bed every day

______

2 we / speak when the teacher is speaking

______

3 my classmates and I / go to school in summer

______

4 Write questions and then complete the interview.

what subjects / you / have to / take / at school?
you / have to / play / with it?
how long / you / have to / study / at university?
you / have to / buy / any special equipment for your snake?
what / he / have to / do / there?
how often / you / have to / feed / your snake?

Interviewer: This is Sasha Miles. She's crazy about animals and she's got a pet snake. Sasha, [1] ______

Sasha: Yes, you need to keep pet snakes in a vivarium. It's very hot in there.

Interviewer: [2] ______

Sasha: Only once a week! And I have to give it fresh water twice a week.

Interviewer: [3] ______

Sasha: You don't have to, but I do because I love holding it. I love animals. I want to be a vet when I'm older.

Interviewer: [4] ______

Sasha: You have to do Biology and Chemistry, and then another subject like Maths or Physics.

Interviewer: [5] ______

Sasha: For five years! My cousin wants to be a vet, too. He's got a part-time job in a vet's.

Interviewer: [6] ______

Sasha: He has to clean the floor and the cages.

5 Write a paragraph about the rules and obligations in your house. Use the ideas in the box or your own ideas. Use *mustn't*, *have to* or *don't have to*.

bedtime homework loud music mealtimes TV

______

LISTENING

1 Read the advert. Match the words in bold with the definitions. Use a dictionary if you need to.

CLIMB TO THE SUMMIT OF THE SYDNEY HARBOUR BRIDGE...

... and experience panoramic views of Australia's largest city. Climbs take place with an expert **guide** throughout the day from **dawn** to **sunset**. You can even climb at night.
All **safety equipment** is provided. All climbers receive a photo as a **souvenir** of their trip.

1 ____________ : Early in the morning when light first appears.
2 ____________ : The top of something, e.g. a mountain.
3 ____________ : Something to remind you of a holiday or a special experience.
4 ____________ : Things you use to keep you safe.
5 ____________ : In the evening when the sun disappears from the sky.
6 ____________ : A person who shows you what to do / where to go.

2 (23) Listen to an interview with Joel. What is his job?

He is...
A an engineer B a builder C a guide D a sales representative

3 (23) Listen again and tick (✓) the correct box.

1 Joel ... in Australia.
- A lives permanently ☐
- B is on holiday ☐
- C is spending 12 months ☐

2 Joel ... to have a job in an office.
- A has ☐
- B really wants ☐
- C doesn't want ☐

3 You ... be fit to do Joel's job.
- A must ☐
- B mustn't ☐
- C don't have to ☐

4 Joel thinks it's best to climb the bridge ... .
- A late at night ☐
- B early in the morning ☐
- C during the day ☐

5 Joel ... different people every day.
- A can't stand meeting ☐
- B loves meeting ☐
- C doesn't meet ☐

6 ... can take a camera on the bridge.
- A Nobody ☐
- B A climber ☐
- C Joel ☐

TEST YOUR MEMORY!

4 Answer the questions.

1 Where is Joel from?
____
2 How many times a day does he climb the bridge?
____
3 How high is the bridge?
____
4 Do any Australians climb the bridge?
____
5 Where exactly does Joel take a photo of the climbers?
____
6 What is Jan scared of?
____

5 Write these sentences in your language.

1 And, you know, I have to do it ten times a day.
____
2 'Do you know how high the bridge is?' 'I haven't got a clue!'
____
3 Come on, it's an amazing experience!
____

READING

1 Who is the webpage for? Read the texts quickly and choose the correct answer.

A young children B teenagers C adults D elderly people

ADVICE LINE

1 *I've got a part-time job in a café with a friend of mine, but she gets more money than me because she's 11 months older. It isn't fair. We do the same things, clearing tables, sweeping the floor, etc. In fact, I think I'm more hard-working than her. What should I do?*
Olivia

Answer: ____________

2 *I'm a member of a swimming club and I train five times a week. Two sessions are before school, from 5.30–7am! I'm always really tired on those days and I keep falling asleep in class. My marks are getting worse. I don't know what to do.*
Sadie

Answer: ____________

3 *I'm 15 and I love going out at the weekend, but places like the cinema or the ice rink are really expensive. I get pocket money, but it isn't enough. You have to be 16 to work in a shop and I can't work with animals because I'm allergic to them. Have you got any tips?*
Jason

Answer: ____________

A There isn't much you can do. Your employer is allowed to decide their rates of pay and, until you're 18, they can vary depending on age. You could look for a better-paid job.

B People your age are allowed to babysit or do gardening jobs. You should make a leaflet about yourself and what you want to do. Then you should deliver it to people in your neighbourhood. Don't forget to put your contact details on it and your rates of pay.

C To get a job or go to university, you need to study hard and pass your exams. Your free-time activities shouldn't affect your education. You should talk to your trainer. You shouldn't stop completely, but are you allowed to have a break?

2 Read the texts again. Match questions 1–3 with answers A–C.

3 Read the texts again and write the names of the people; Jason, Sadie or Olivia.

Who...

1 gets up very early? __________
2 keeps a place clean? __________
3 isn't old enough to be a shop assistant? __________
4 has a problem with pets? __________
5 is unhappy with her rate of pay? __________
6 does a tiring activity? __________
7 works harder than her friend? __________
8 should stop doing something for a while? __________

EXTRA WORD ZONE

Tip and *advice*

4 Complete the definitions with tip or advice.

1 ________________, *uncount n.*
When you tell someone what they should do.
My ~ is to go to the doctor's.

2 ________________, *count n.*
A small piece of useful advice.
Here's a ~ on how to get a job.

5 Complete the sentences with *tip*, *tips* or *advice*.

1 How many __________ are on the website?
2 'Did he give you any good __________?'
'No, not much.'
3 Is there much __________ in the article?
4 Have you got a(n)__________ on how to learn irregular verbs?

VOCABULARY Household chores

6 Circle the correct verb.

1 **load / feed / make** the dog
2 **sweep / hang out / water** the plants
3 **lay / make / do** the bed
4 **take out / put away / take** the dog for a walk
5 **clean / sweep / make** the car
6 **put away / water / feed** the groceries
7 **do / make / take out** the rubbish
8 **clean / water / sweep** the floor

7 Complete the sentences with the verbs in the box.

clear do (x3) hang out lay load

Before you have dinner, you have to 1 __________ the table.
After the meal, you have to 2 __________ the table and 3 __________ the dishwasher. If you haven't got a dishwasher, you have to 4 __________ the washing up.
When your clothes are dirty, you have to 5 __________ the washing. When it's ready, you have to 6 __________ the washing in the garden.
When the clothes are dry, you have to 7 __________ the ironing.

8 Write about the chores you and your family do. Include the adverbs of frequency in brackets.

1 (never) __________
2 (hardly ever) __________
3 (often) __________
4 (always) __________

WANT TO KNOW MORE? Things connected to household chores

9 Match the words 1-5 with A-E to make compound nouns. Then write the words under the correct picture. Use a dictionary if you need to.

1 washing	A cleaner
2 table	B machine
3 ironing	C board
4 rubbish	D cloth
5 vacuum	E bin

1 __ 2 __ 3 __ 4 __ 5 __

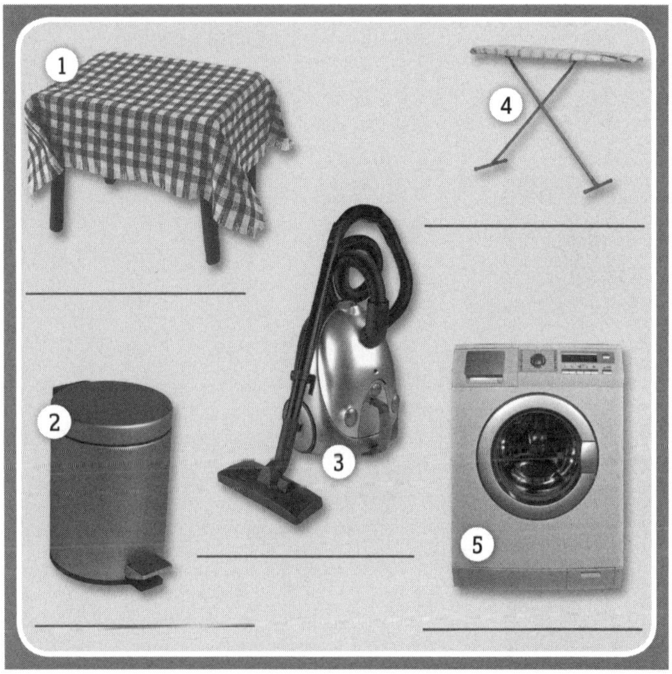

10 Write sentences about the chores you do with the things in exercise 10.

1 *You put the rubbish in a rubbish bin.*
2 __________
3 __________
4 __________
5 __________
6 __________

11 Choose three of the things in exercise 10. Write true sentences about you. How often do you use them?

1 __________
2 __________
3 __________

GRAMMAR Modals: permission, advice & suggestions

1 Complete the sentences with the correct form of *be allowed to* and the verbs in the box.

park play ride smoke take walk

1 You ______________________________ through the nature reserve.

2 We ______________________________ our dog for a walk on that beach.

3 People ______________________________ their bikes on the cycle path.

4 My dad ______________________________ golf there.

5 People ______________________________ their cars on that street.

6 You ______________________________ in that area.

2 Rewrite the sentences so that they mean the same. Use *be allowed to / not be allowed to* or *can / can't*.

1 I can't stay out late tonight.
I ____.
2 They're allowed to wear trainers to school.
They ____.
3 Millie isn't allowed to have a piercing.
Millie ____.
4 We can't go into that bar.
We ____.
5 Rafa can get a part-time job.
Rafa ____.
6 You aren't allowed to take photos in the museum.
You ____.

3 Complete the exchanges with *should* and *shouldn't* and the verbs in the box.

do feed hang study wear

1 **James:** I haven't got any clean clothes.
Dan: You ____________________________ the washing.
2 **Sue:** Lara loves looking after sick people.
Mary: She ____________________________ to be a nurse.
3 **Ben:** Is it raining?
Tom: Yes. You ____________________________ out the washing right now.
4 **John:** My brother can't see very well.
Mark: He ____________________________ glasses.
5 **Sam:** Their dog is very fat.
Aaron: They ____________________________ it so often.

4 Complete the dialogue with *should / shouldn't* or *need*.

Enzo: I'm really tired.
Nadia: You [1] ________________ go to bed earlier.
Enzo: But when I go to bed, I can't sleep. What [2] ________________ I do?
Nadia: You [3] ________________ to do things to help you relax.
Enzo: Like what?
Nadia: You [4] ________________ listen to relaxing music before going to bed or have a warm drink.
Enzo: What? Like coffee?
Nadia: No! You [5] ________________ drink coffee because it contains caffeine.
Enzo: OK. Thanks!

5 Match the words in the boxes to make phrases. Then, write suggestions for the problems below with *could* and the phrases you have formed.

set put away take out look it up	in a dictionary your alarm clock the groceries the rubbish

1 *The kitchen smells awful.*
____

2 *I don't know what that word means.*
____

3 *I need to get up early tomorrow.*
____

4 *There's no space on the table.*
____

EXTRA CHALLENGE

Think of a job for a teenager. Use the suggestions below or your own ideas.

HELP WANTED CLEANING CARS

TEENAGER NEEDED TO DELIVER LEAFLETS

SUMMER CAMP HELPER WANTED

HELP NEEDED ON A CHICKEN FARM

Write an advert for the job you have chosen. Describe the things you have to do in that job and the qualities you need. Don't forget to include the hours and the rate of pay.

WEBQUEST

Go online and find the answers to the questions.

1 Which plant does chocolate come from?

____

2 Where is the tallest waterslide in the world? What is it called?

____

3 What language does the word *chef* come from?

____

4 What is the telephone number for the emergency services in the UK?

____

5 What is the minimum rate of pay for a 16–17 year old in the UK?

____

6 At what age can you leave school in the UK?

____

PUZZLE

Copy every other letter to make a sentence. Are the sentences true for you? Tick (✓) TRUE or FALSE .

1 IKHRABVQELTPOFWYEXAPRGGOLTACSISUECS

______________________ TRUE ☐ FALSE ☐

2 IJDTOBND'ETSHIAWVPEOTFOWLXAUYETNHQELTBALBOLYE

______________________ TRUE ☐ FALSE ☐

3 INMWUCSOTOTNALKOEHAVBLUPSWTLODSVCQHPOLOGL

______________________ TRUE ☐ FALSE ☐

4 IWNAEQEZDCTKOFPSRZABCHTOIQSLEHMLYSEFNOGULWIFSWH

______________________ TRUE ☐ FALSE ☐

INTERACTION Understanding problems and giving advice

1 Answer the questions. Can you remember how to express yourself?

What do you say ...

1 to ask how someone is when they've got a problem?
____
2 to advise someone to eat more fruit?
____
3 to advise someone not to stay up late?
____
4 to express doubt about someone's advice?
____
5 accept someone's advice?
____

2 (24) Circle the correct words. Listen and check.

Sue: What's [1] **in / up / down**?
Tom: I keep getting headaches.
Sue: Why don't you drink more water?
Tom: [2] **I / I'd / I'll** try that.

Aidan: [3] **Who's / How's / What's** wrong?
Adrianna: I'm really bored.
Aidan: You could [4] **go / to go / going** to the cinema.
Adrianna: The trouble is, I've got no money.

Adam: Are you OK?
Dorothy: I'm really hot.
Adam: You [5] **would / should / shouldn't** take off your jacket.
Dorothy: That's [6] **bad / good / a good** idea.

3 Read the dialogue and answer the questions.

Beth: Hi, Tara. Are you OK?
Tara: Not really. I've lost my mobile.
Beth: Oh, no. Where do you think it is?
Tara: I've been shopping so I think it's in one of the shops.
Beth: You should go back and look for it.
Tara: The trouble is, I've been in loads of shops. I can't remember all of them.
Beth: Why don't you phone your number?
Tara: I'm not sure that's a good idea.
Beth: Yes, it is. If someone answers it, you could ask which shop they're in. Then you could go and get it.
Tara: That's a good idea! But ... I haven't got a phone.
Beth: You can use mine. Your number's in the list of contacts.
Tara: Thank you, Beth. That's great.

1 What is Tara's problem?
____
2 Where did this happen?
____
3 Why can't she go and look for it?
____
4 What advice does Beth give Tara?
____
5 Does Tara accept this advice immediately?
____
6 Whose mobile does Tara use?
____

4 Complete the dialogue.

You: (Ask Harry what the problem is.)
1 _______________
Harry: I'm nervous about my exams.
You: (Give him a piece of advice.)
2 _______________
Harry: Do you think so?
You: (Give him another piece of advice.)
3 _______________
Harry: I'm not sure that's a good idea.
You: (Make a suggestion.)
4 _______________
Harry: OK. I'll try that.

YOUR TURN TO SPEAK

5 (25) Revise the *Express yourself* box on page 90 of the Student's Book. Then listen to the people and respond.

WRITING An email about rules in a club

WRITING SKILL Using adverbs

1 Circle the correct adverb.

1 He's **almost / quite** strict.
2 I love playing for Bradley Juniors, **only / especially** when I score a goal.
3 It has **just / also** over 200 players.
4 I **nearly / really** hope you join the club.
5 Sometimes we play a match **instead / almost**.
6 We **only / quite** play them on Sundays.
7 There are **also / instead** four girls' teams.
8 It costs **really / almost** £150 a year to be a member of the club.

2 Complete the text with the sentences in exercise 1.

From: Ben H
To: Louis
Subject: My football club

Dear Louis,

You wanted to know about my football club, so let me tell you a bit about it.

I'm a member of Bradley Juniors Football Club.
1 ______.
There are ten teams, from under 9s to under 18s.
2 ______.
My friend Rosa plays for one of them.
The U14 team has football practice from 7–8pm on Fridays. We do fitness and skills training.
3 ______.
Our coach is called Bruce.
4 ______.
We have to work hard!
5 ______.
That includes your training kit and match kit. We don't play our matches on Saturdays.
6 ______.
Bruce always checks our football boots before a match. You aren't allowed to play with dirty boots!
7 ______.
I've scored three goals this season. One of them was brilliant!
8 ______.
We need a good defender like you. If you need to know anything else, just email me.

Ben

3 Read the text again and circle T (true) or F (false).

1 Girls aren't allowed to play for Bradley Juniors. T / F
2 Ben has to train on Friday evenings. T / F
3 You have to pay to join Bradley Juniors. T / F
4 You must wear your own clothes when you play. T / F
5 Ben plays his matches at the weekend. T / F
6 You mustn't have dirty boots before a match. T / F
7 Ben can't stand playing for his club. T / F
8 Louis plays for Bradley Juniors Football Club. T / F

4 Look at the *Writing Reference* on page 120. Then write an email to a friend about a sports club or youth club that you are a member of. Invent the details if necessary. Include some adverbs. Write about:

– the number of members
– the activities
– the person in charge
– the club rules
– your opinion of the club

Reminder

- *Check your modals for rules and obligation.*
- *Check your adverbs.*

9 Out and about

READING

1 Read the texts. Match headings A–D with 1–3. There is one heading you don't need.

A Web postings
B What's on in the Studio
C How to find us
D About us

2 Read the texts again. Circle T (true), F (false) or DS (doesn't say).

1 The Lowry is in an old building. **T / F / DS**
2 You can see L.S. Lowry's paintings in the art gallery. **T / F / DS**
3 It's free to go in the art gallery. **T / F / DS**
4 The classes take place in one of the main theatres. **T / F / DS**
5 The art classes take place at the weekend. **T / F / DS**

EXTRA WORD ZONE

Adjectives / Adverbs connected to time

4 Complete the definitions with words from the texts.

1 ______________ : happening every day
2 ______________ : happening every week
3 ______________ : happening every month
4 ______________ : happening every year

THE LOWRY ART CENTRE

1 ______________

The Lowry is an arts centre in a modern building in Salford near Manchester. Named after the famous local artist L.S. Lowry (1887–1976), the Lowry opened in April 2000. It has two theatres and a smaller studio, and it presents a variety of shows including drama, musicals, opera, dance, comedy and music. It also has an art gallery where you can see the famous works of L.S. Lowry and temporary exhibitions of other artists. With a restaurant, cafés and bars, the Lowry is a must-see tourist attraction.

2 ______________

Contemporary dance workshop for students aged 11 – 17
Class size: 30
Tickets: £3per class
Time: Weekly from 5pm to 6pm

Art classes for beginners aged 14+
Class size: 15
Tickets: £28
Time: Monthly from 11am to 3.30pm on Saturday and Sunday

Learn about dance and drama at our yearly summer school
Class size: 45 (8 – 16 years)
Tickets: £70
Time: 10am-5pm daily during August

3 ______________

I'm doing the summer school again in July. It was brilliant last year. We're going to perform in front of our family on the final day.
Amy

Is anyone doing the contemporary dance workshop?
Billy

I'm doing the dance workshop on the 17th August. I booked it yesterday. Get a place in the same class!
Alex

My cousins are visiting from the USA next week. We're going to take them to the Lowry and show them Lowry's paintings. I hope they like them!
Margot

3 Read the texts again and answer the questions.

1 How did the Lowry get its name?
____
2 When did it open?
____
3 Where can you have something to eat and drink?
____
4 How long are the dance classes?
____
5 Who has done a class at the Lowry before?
____

5 Complete the sentences with the words in exercise 4.

1 They have a ______________ skiing holiday in February.
2 I've got a part-time job. They pay me ______________, on Fridays.
3 *The Times* is a ______________ newspaper in the UK.
4 It's a ______________ magazine so I get it 12 times a year.

VOCABULARY Places in a town

6 Write the words in the box under the correct heading.

art gallery bookshop coffee shop museum
newsagents police station sandwich bar
sports centre stadium town hall

1 Food and drink

2 Sports

3 History and the arts

4 Law and local government

5 Books and the media

7 Match these places with the questions and requests. There is one place you don't need

bank department store hotel internet café
library park pharmacy restaurant theatre

I'd like to book a double room, please.
1 ____________

I'd like to take out £100, please.
2 ____________

How much does it cost to go online for an hour?
3 ____________

Have you got anything for a bad headache?
4 ____________

Which floor are ladies' shoes on?
5 ____________

What time does the play start?
6 ____________

I'd like to borrow these books, please.
7 ____________

Can we have the bill, please?
8 ____________

8 Write about the places in town you and your family go to using the adverbs of frequency.

1 (always) ____________

2 (often) ____________

3 (hardly ever) ____________

WANT TO KNOW MORE? Things in places in town

9 Complete the signs with the words in the box. Use a dictionary if you need to.

desk machine office room till trolley

10 Read the sentences and write the words in exercise 9.

1 You take out money from here at any time.

2 You buy tickets in a cinema or theatre from here.

3 You put your things in this while you're doing the shopping in a supermarket.

4 You try on clothes here in a department store.

5 You go here to pay for things in a shop.

6 You check in or out of a hotel here.

11 Write three sentences using some of the words in exercise 9.

You have to have £1 to use the shopping trolleys in our supermarket.

GRAMMAR Future plans & intentions

1 Look at Kate's diary. Complete the text about her arrangements. Use the present continuous form of the verbs in the box.

	July 3		July 4
am	• 10.35 train to London • British Museum	am	• 11.00 meet Mum & Dad • go to Wimbledon
pm	• dinner with William @ Hard Rock Café	pm	• Men's Quarter Final

go have take visit watch

Kate [1] ______ the train to London at 10.35. Then she [2] ______ the British Museum. In the evening, Kate and her friend William [3] ______ a meal in a restaurant.

The next day, Kate [4] ______ to Wimbledon with her parents. One of the matches they [5] ______ is the Men's Quarter Final.

2 Complete the questions with the present continuous form of the verbs in brackets and answer them.

1 At what time ______ (Kate / travel) to London on 3rd July?
______

2 What museum ______ (Kate / visit) that morning?
______

3 Where ______ (Kate and William / have) dinner that evening?
______

4 Who ______ (Kate / meet) at 11 o'clock the next morning?
______

5 ______ (Kate and her parents / play) tennis at Wimbledon?
______

3 Think about your arrangements for tomorrow. Write one affirmative and one negative sentence.

1 ______

2 ______

4 Complete the text with the correct form of *be going to* and the verbs in brackets.

Grant is crazy about sport and usually goes to the sports centre five times a week. However, he [1] ______ (not do) any sport for a while because [2] ______ (take) some important exams at school soon. He [3] ______ (not watch) TV either and he and his mates [4] ______ (not hang out) at the park. Instead, Grant [5] ______ (stay) at home in the evenings and he [6] ______ (study) hard for his exams.

5 Write the words in the correct order to make questions. Then complete the answers with the correct form of *be going to* and the verbs in brackets

Teacher: [1] what / to / you / are / going / when you're older / do?
______?
Grant: I [2] ______ (be) a teacher at secondary school.
Teacher: [3] a Maths teacher / be / are / going / to / you?
______?
Grant: No, I'm not. I [4] ______ (teach) P.E.
Teacher: [5] going / are / to / you / study at / which university?
______?
Grant: I'm not sure, but I [6] ______ (not study) in the UK.
Teacher: [7] you and your friends / going / what / are / when school finishes / do / to?
______?
Grant: We [8] ______ (relax) and have fun!
Teacher: [9] on holiday / you and your family / going / to / go / are?
______?
Grant: Yes. We [10] ______ (visit) my aunt and uncle. They live in France.

6 Write true answers about you.

1 What are you going to study when you're older?
______

2 What are you going to do when school finishes?
______

3 Who are you going to spend your summer holidays with? Where?
______

LISTENING

1 Match the places in the box with the pictures. Then match the verbs with the correct places. Use a dictionary if you need to.

dance floor funfair stage tent

to camp to dance to go on rides to perform

1

______
______

2

______
______

3

______
______

4

______
______

2 26 Listen to a conversation between Lara and Leo. What are they chatting about?

A a town carnival
B a music festival
C a dance competition
D a birthday party

3 26 Listen again and complete the factfile.

1 What is the name of the event?

2 Where is it?

3 How long does it last?

4 How many stages are there?

5 What types of music can you hear?

6 Where can you dance?

7 What else is there to do or see?

TEST YOUR MEMORY!

4 Answer the questions.

1 How old is Leo going to be on Saturday?
______

2 How many bedrooms are there in Lara's tent?
______

3 Are you allowed to take dogs?
______

4 Which pop singer is Lara going to see?
______

5 What day does Lara ask Leo to come?
______

5 Write these sentences in your language.

1 'That sounds boring.' 'You are so wrong, Leo!'
______

2 'It's a special dance floor in a big tent.' 'That sounds fun!'
______

3 You won't regret it!
______

READING

1 Read the article quickly and choose a suitable title.

A **More than just communication** B **Electronic devices through the ages** C **Digital entertainment**

2 Read the article again. Put the paragraphs in order.

A __

What will our mobile phones be like in the future? They'll be a similar size, but they'll probably have special screens that expand. This will make it easier to read documents. Your phone will also be your identification, such as your passport or driving licence. If you travel abroad, you won't need to take your passport. You'll show your phone at passport control.

__ **C**

Mobile phones have changed a lot since the first completely portable mobile phone appeared in 1983. The DynaTAC 8000X was around 33 cm long and weighed just under a kilogram. You could store 30 phone numbers in it and its battery gave you an hour of talk time. The quality of calls wasn't very good and you were often cut off while you were talking.

B __

Mobile phones today are very different, not just in appearance (they fit in our pockets now), but also in performance. These devices allow us to multitask. We use them to send text messages and emails, browse the internet, watch films, listen to music, take pictures, record videos, play video games and, of course, make calls.

__ **D**

As a result, you won't be able to live without your mobile phone. If you lose it, you'll be able to contact your supplier and they'll deliver a new one the next day. All your data will already be on it, so you'll be able to use it straight away. If someone finds your old phone, it won't be any use to them because you'll be able to lock it remotely.

3 Read the text again and tick (✓) YES or NO.

		YES	NO
1	You could put the DynaTAC 8000X in your pocket.	☐	☐
2	In the DynaTAC8000X, you couldn't save any telephone number of any contact.	☐	☐
3	Mobile phones look different today.	☐	☐
4	They have more than one function.	☐	☐
5	Mobile phones will be much smaller in the future.	☐	☐
6	In the future, people will still use traditional passports only.	☐	☐
7	It'll take a week to get a new mobile if you lose yours.	☐	☐
8	There will be a system to protect your phone from other users.	☐	☐

WORD ZONE EXTRA

Wordbuilding

4 Find the nouns of these verbs in the text. One of them doesn't appear.

Verb	Noun
appear	1
perform	2
identify	3
control	4

5 Complete the sentences with the correct verb or noun in exercise 4.

1 Your ________________ has changed. You look different!
2 Parents should ________________ the things that young children can look at on the internet.
3 A computer's ________________ depends on the speed of its processor.
4 Can you ________________ the person who stole your mobile?

VOCABULARY Digital entertainment

6 Do the crossword.

Across

2 You video people with this.

3 This prints your documents.

Down

1 A camera on your computer so that people can see you online.

4 The part of a computer where the keys are.

5 This is connected to the computer. You use it to move around the screen.

7 Match the words from both boxes to complete the sentences.

digital disc hard High Definition MP3 remote surround sound USB

camera control dock drive player port speakers TV

1 Where's the ________ ________?
I want to change channels on the TV.

2 There's an ________ ________
in the car, so you can play your MP3 player.

3 My new mobile phone is also a ________
________. It takes great photos.

4 I love watching films on our new ________
________.

5 You can't save the file because the ________
________ is full.

6 You can't play DVDs in a Blu-ray ________
________.

7 You have to put the memory stick into a ________
________ in your computer.

8 It's like being at a concert when you listen to music through ________ ________.

8 Write true sentences for you about the digital technology that you and your family members have.

____

____

____

____

WANT TO KNOW MORE?

Words connected to a computer

9 Read the adverts. Match the words underlined with the definitions. Use a dictionary if you need to.

1 Emails that you don't want. ________

2 A copy of a file or document. ________

3 A secret code. ________

4 The picture that appears on your desktop when you aren't using your computer. ________

5 Any information on your computer, e.g. files, photos, games, emails, songs... ________

10 Read the text and circle the correct words.

I received a [1] **spam / password** email yesterday. When I opened it, a virus started attacking my computer. It destroyed all the [2] **data / screensavers** on it. Fortunately, I had a [3] **backup / spam** of everything.

I'm going to get some new anti-virus software to protect my computer and I'm going to use a [4] **backup / password** so that I'm the only person who can log on to it.

11 Write three true sentences for you. Include some of the words in exercise 9.

1 ____

2 ____

3 ____

9 GRAMMAR *will* for predictions | First conditional

1 Complete the text with *will* or *won't* and the verbs in the box.

be not buy not come get have invite make

My sister, Emma, 1 ______________________ 18 this year. It's an important birthday in the UK, so I think she 2 ______________________ a big present from us. I think we 3 ______________________ a big party and she 4 ______________________ lots of friends and relatives. Dad 5 ______________________ a big cake too. He's good at cooking so, he 6 ______________________ one from the supermarket. Our dog is scared of loud music so he 7 ______________________ to the party.

2 Reorder the words to make questions. Then complete the answers in the exchanges with *will* or *won't*.

1 (get / will / in the next year / you / a new mobile)
______________________________?
Yes, I ____________. I think I ____________ get a white one.

2 (will / on Saturday / the weather / what / be like)
______________________________?
It ____________ be hot and it ____________ rain. It hardly ever rains in July.

3 (you're older / you / famous / be / will /when)
______________________________?
No, I ____________. I think I ____________ have a quiet life.

3 Write true answers for you to these questions. Give as much information as possible.

1 Do you think you will get a new computer soon?
____

2 Where will you go on holiday next summer?
____

3 What will you be when you grow up?
____

4 Complete the sentences with an *If* clause or a main clause.

if I find a pharmacy if it rains
if I can watch 3D films on my television

you'll feel sick we'll have to walk home
you won't be able to get up early

1 I won't hang out the washing ______________________.
2 If we miss the bus, ______________________.
3 I'll get some medicine ______________________.
4 If you don't go to sleep, ______________________.
5 I won't go the cinema ______________________.
6 If you eat all that food, ______________________.

5 Complete the dialogue with the correct form of the verbs in the box.

not be borrow go lose start take

Lara: What will you do if you 1 ____________ your key?
Tom: I 2 ____________ to the neighbours because they've got a spare one.
Lara: If they 3 ____________ in, where will you go?
Tom: I 4 ____________ the bus into town and go to the library.
Lara: 5 ____________ you ____________ a book if you go there?
Tom: No, I won't. I 6 ____________ doing my homework.

6 Complete the first conditional sentences with the correct form of the verbs in brackets.

I don't know what to do next weekend but there are lots of things happening in Oxford. Let's see...

If I 1 ____________ (be) there on Sunday, I 2 ____________ (visit) the Pitt Rivers Museum, but I 3 ____________ (not do) the theatre workshop. I don't enjoy acting. If it 4 ____________ (not rain), I 5 ____________ (have) a picnic by the river with some friends, but we 6 ____________ (not hire) a punt. I'm sure I 7 ____________ (take) lots of photos if I 8 ____________ (walk) round one of the colleges in Oxford, they're beautiful...

7 Complete the sentences so that they are true for you.

1 If I go to university, ______________________.
2 ______________________ if I go to a football match.
3 If I get some money, ______________________.
4 ______________________ if my parents go out tonight.

EXTRA CHALLENGE

This is Jacob. Imagine you have just met each other and you're having a conversation with him. Plan the questions you're going to ask him. Each question should have a follow-up question. Use the pictures to help you. Write your questions and invent Jacob's answers.

WEBQUEST

Go online and find the answers to the questions.

1 What are the opening hours of the Pitt Rivers Museum in Oxford?

____

2 The section of the River Thames that is in Oxford has got a different name. What is it?

____

3 What was the Latin name for the town of Devizes?

____

4 Where exactly is the town hall in Devizes?

____

5 If you phone the UK from your country, what code do you have to use before the phone number?

____

6 John Logie Baird was the first person to show moving pictures on TV. What nationality was he? What was his job?

____

PUZZLE

Copy the words with the same symbols. Put them in order to make questions. Then write true answers.

you ☺	the ❄	the ¤	going ☺	doing ¤
at ¤	win ❄	to ☺	weekend ¤	next ❄
tomorrow ☺	will ❄	are ¤	jeans ☺	What ¤
who ❄	are ☺	you ¤	World Cup ❄	wear ☺

¤ Question: ______________________________?
Answer: ______________________________

❄ Question: ______________________________?
Answer: ______________________________

☺ Question: ______________________________?
Answer: ______________________________

INTERACTION Asking for and giving directions

1 Answer the questions. Can you remember how to express yourself?

What do you say ...

1 to get someone's attention before you ask them a question?

____

2 to ask for directions to the sports centre?

____

3 to tell someone to continue without turning left or right?

____

2 27 Complete the exchanges with words in the box. Listen and check.

cross go turn where

David: Excuse me, [1] ______________'s the nearest bank?
Alisha: [2] ______________ down this road and [3] ______________ left.
David: Left... OK.
Alisha: Then [4] ______________ the road and the bank is on the right.
David: Thanks.

corner go take tell

Kevin: Can you [5] ______________ me where the supermarket is, please?
Dorothy: Sure. [6] ______________ the second right and go straight on.
Kevin: Is that Oak Street?
Dorothy: Yes, it is. [7] ______________ to the end of that street. The supermarket is on the [8] ______________ of Oak Street and Stamford Road.

when town traffic how

Lessie: Excuse me, [9] ______________ do I get to the bus station?
Ray: At the [10] ______________ lights, turn right and go straight on for about 200 metres.
Lessie: OK.
Ray: [11] ______________ you get to the [12] ______________ hall, turn left and it's at the end of the road.

3 Read the dialogue and circle T (true) or F (false).

Sam: Excuse me, I'm trying to find a sandwich bar called *Snacks*. Do you know where it is?
Girl 1: I'm sorry, I don't. I'm a tourist here.
Sam: Excuse me, can you tell me where *Snacks* is?
Girl 2: Yes, go to the end of this road and turn right.
Sam: OK.
Girl 2: Then take the second... no, hang on... the third right.
Sam: The third right, OK.
Girl 2: There's a big supermarket at the end of that road and *Snacks* is next to it, on the left.
Sam: Great! Thanks. How long does it take to get there on foot?
Girl 2: About 15 minutes. There's also a good sandwich bar called *Mama's* on the corner of this street. You could go there instead.
Sam: Oh, it's OK, thanks. I'm meeting a friend in *Snacks* at 12.30.
Girl 2: OK. Good bye.
Sam: Thanks. Bye.

1 The first girl can't help Sam. T / F
2 The second girl knows exactly where *Snacks* is. T / F
3 It's inside a supermarket. T / F
4 It takes about a quarter of an hour to walk there. T / F
5 *Snacks* is much nearer than *Mama's*. T / F

4 Complete the dialogue.

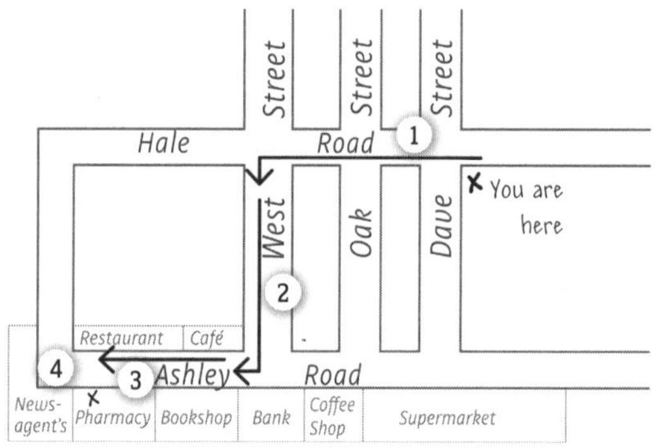

Man: Excuse me, where's the nearest pharmacy?
You: (Give him the first direction.)
1 ______________________________
Man: What's the name of that road?
You: It's called West Street. (Give him the second direction.)
2 ______________________________
Man: OK.
You: (Give him the third direction.)
3 ______________________________
Man: Yeah.
You: (Give him the fourth direction and describe the location of the pharmacy in relation to the other shops.)
4 ______________________________
Man: Great! Thanks very much. Bye.

YOUR TURN TO SPEAK

5 28 Revise the *Express yourself* box on page 100 of the Student's Book. Then listen to the people and respond.

WRITING A report

WRITING SKILL Reporting statistics

1 Reorder the words and complete the sentences.

1 (person / one / only)
_________________________ is going to wait for the DVD.

2 (them / some / of)
___________________ buy sweets from the supermarket.

3 (I / to / everyone / spoke)
_________________________ enjoys going to the cinema.

4 (no / group / the / in / one)
______________________ enjoys watching horror films.

5 (them / of / two / only)
_____________________________________ go every week.

2 Complete the text with the sentences in exercise 1.

> **My report**
> by Tony
>
> For this report I spoke to ten people in the street. I wanted to find out about their cinema habits and routines. [1] ______________________
>
> However, they don't go to the cinema regularly. [2] ______________________
>
> They've got student discount cards, so it's cheaper.
>
> Six of the people buy popcorn at the cinema. The others think that cinema food is too expensive. [3] ______________________
>
> Almost all of them take a bottle of water into the cinema.
>
> All of the people I spoke to love seeing action films and comedies.
> [4] ______________________
>
> Most of them are going to see the latest James Bond film.
> [5] ______________________
>
> Going to the cinema is a popular free-time activity, but everyone thinks that tickets should be cheaper.

3 Read the report again and circle the correct words.

Tony did a survey about going to the cinema with ten [1] **friends / relatives / strangers**. The people he spoke to who go to the cinema [2] **daily / weekly / monthly** are students. [3] **Just under half / Half / Just over half** of the people eat popcorn from the cinema during a film. The rest prefer getting things from [4] **the newsagent's / the supermarket / the cinema**. Action films and comedies are popular with [5] **everyone / no one / one person**. Horror films are [6] **very / the most / the least** popular.

4 Look at the *Writing Reference* on page 121. Then write a short summary report. Use the results of a questionnaire below. Include some expressions for reporting statistics.

> **Speak to ten people who are visiting the British Museum in London this weekend.**
>
> - Where are you from? — *The UK* |||||| — *Other countries* ||||
> - Do you enjoy visiting museums? — *Yes* ||||||||| — *No* |
> - Have you been to the British Museum before? — *Yes* — *No* ||||||||||
> - Are you going to have lunch in the museum café? — *Yes* |||| — *No* ||||||
> - Are you going to go to the gift shop? — *Yes* |||||||||| — *No*
> - Do you think you'll buy a souvenir? — *Yes* ||||| — *No* |||||

> **Reminder**
> - Check your verb forms.
> - Check your expressions for reporting statistics.

My report

____

____

____

____

____

____

____

____

____

____

____

____

____

____

____

____

____

____

____

____

Review Units 7-9

VOCABULARY

1 Write the words under the correct headings.

builder cheerful mouse park pilot plump printer serious short shy slim speakers stadium town hall vet

Appearance	
Jobs	
Places in town	
Personality	
Technology	

2 Circle the correct prepositions.

1 I hate putting **down / up / away** the groceries.
2 You're quite good **in / at / on** speaking English.
3 How often do you do the washing **out / up / of**?
4 She's crazy **about / for / into** animals.
5 Can you hang **into / on / out** the washing, please?
6 Are you keen **in / of / on** reading?

3 Complete the text with the words in the box.

adores architect art eyes library piercing wavy

My aunt has got long, [1] ____________, fair hair and blue [2] ____________. She's also got a [3] ____________ in her nose. She's a creative person and she [4] ____________ drawing. She's an [5] ____________ so she designs buildings for her job. She's designed the new [6] ____________ in our town. She's designing an [7] ____________ gallery now.

GRAMMAR

4 Complete the sentences with the words in the box.

been ever for gone have must mustn't since

1 You ____________ touch that snake. It's dangerous.
2 He's been a firefighter ____________ 2010.
3 I ____________ go home now.
4 Suzi isn't here. She's ____________ to school.
5 I've known Sarah ____________ a long time.
6 We ____________ to wear a school uniform.
7 Have you ____________ met a celebrity?
8 I've ____________ shopping I have to put away the groceries.

5 Match the halves of the sentences.

1 I've never	A play tennis more often.
2 We're playing	B tennis on Saturday.
3 I won't play tennis	C 'll win the match.
4 You should	D to wear tennis shoes.
5 You don't have	E played tennis.
6 I think I	F if it rains.

1 __ 2 __ 3 __ 4 __ 5 __ 6 __

6 Complete the sentences with the correct form of the verbs in brackets.

1 How long ____________ (you / live) in London?
2 If you work hard, you ____________ (pass) your exam.
3 I'll phone you if the bus ____________ (not arrive).
4 He ____________ (never / fly) in a helicopter.
5 We ____________ (meet) her friends at four o'clock tomorrow.
6 I ____________ (study) biology at university in September.

REVIEW CHECK

7 Read the facts and choose the correct words.

- There [1] ... a tennis tournament at Wimbledon since 1877.
- All the players [2] ... to wear white clothing at Wimbledon.
- Has a British man ever won the tournament? Yes, [3] ... .
- A British woman [4] ... won the tournament for over 45 years.
- If you [5] ... to Wimbledon, you [6] ... the best tennis players in the world.
- You [7] ... eat strawberries and cream at Wimbledon. It's traditional.
- We [8] ... to the men's final in July. We've got great tickets.
- Fans without tickets are [9] ... queue for tickets in the morning.
- I think Nadal [10] ... Wimbledon this year.

1
A is **B** was **C** has been
2
A must **B** have **C** could
3
A he has **B** she has **C** has
4
A hasn't **B** haven't **C** didn't
5
A 'll go **B** goes **C** go
6
A 're seeing **B** won't see **C** 'll see
7
A shouldn't **B** should **C** have
8
A go **B** 're going **C** 'll go
9
A must **B** allowed **C** allowed to
10
A will win **B** wins **C** is winning

Video

Bollywood

BEFORE YOU WATCH

1 Read the introduction and the questions in NOW WATCH.

Introduction

India produces more films than any other country in the world, including the USA. The most popular style of cinema is Bollywood.

NOW WATCH

2 Answer the questions.

1 Where does the name Bollywood come from?

______

2 What similarities are there with old Hollywood musicals?

______

3 Who are Aishwarya Rai and Sharukh Khan?

______

4 What typical things can you find in Bollywood films?

______

5 Why are the films *Moulin Rouge* and *Slumdog Millionaire* mentioned?

______

FOLLOW UP

3 Go online and find out about Bollywood. Write an interesting fact to share with your class.

Did you know that...?

______

Review Unit 1

CROSSWORD

Across

1 ... you swim? (3)
3 After dinner and before you go to bed, you ... your teeth. (5)
5 If your mother remarries, her new husband is your ... . (10)
6 Before you go to sleep, you have to ... ready for bed. (3)
7 If you have no brothers or sisters, you are a(n) ... child. (4)
9 Your mother or your father's brother is your ... . (5)
10 My brother ... a lot of sport at school. (4)

Down

2 Your uncle's son is your father's ... . (6)
4 I ... ever go to the cinema – maybe once a year. (6)
5 It saves water if you have a(n) ... and not a bath. (6)
8 Your aunt's daughter is your mother's ... .(5)

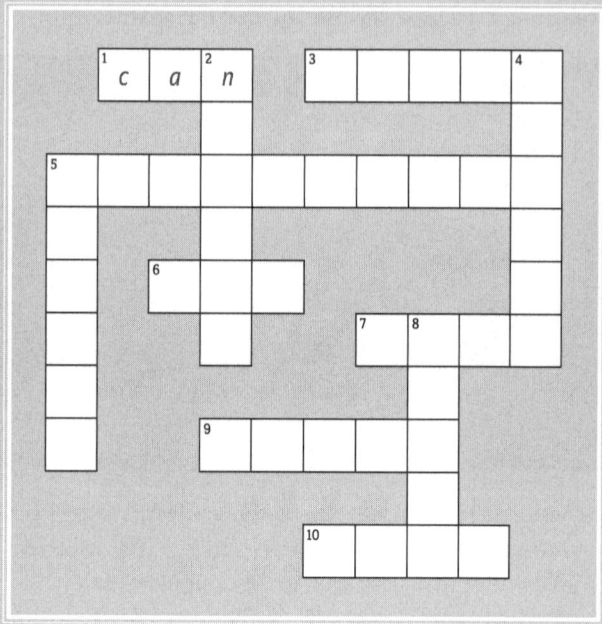

I CAN...

Reading

☐ I can understand an internet profile.
☐ I can understand an article about typical families in Britain.

Vocabulary

☐ I can talk about family.
☐ I can talk about everyday activities.

Grammar

☐ I can use the present simple.
☐ I can use adverbs of frequency.
☐ I can use *can* and *can't to* talk about ability and possibility.

Listening

☐ I can understand an interview with a boy about his new life.

Interaction

☐ I can understand a conversation involving meeting new people.
☐ I can greet and meet new people.

Challenge

☐ I can find out what I have in common with other students.

Writing

☐ I can use some common conjunctions.
☐ I can write a message on a website.

ERROR CORRECTION

1 *My fathers get up very early.*
My parents get up very early.

2 *Jenny like computer games.*

____

3 *I not play football.*

____

4 *Watch you TV after dinner?*

____

5 *'Thanks!' 'No worry!'*

____

6 *I breakfast at eight o'clock.*

____

7 *I listen often to music at home.*

____

8 *I don't can play the piano.*

____

Review Unit 2

CROSSWORD

Across

1 ... is an indoor sport that involves different exercises on the floor and using bars and other equipment. (10)
3 ... you watching this match on TV? (3)
4 My sister ... surfing every weekend. (4)
7 ... is an outdoor sport that can involve running, jumping or throwing.(9)
8 To play ... , you need two teams of 15 players and an egg-shaped ball. (5)
10 I can't talk now. I'm ... tennis. (7)

Down

1 My football club gives us our ... – shirts, shorts, boots and everything. (4)
2 I like skiing, but only on an easy .... (5)
5 My father wants to go ... around the Greek islands this summer. (7)
6 If you're hitting a ball with a round bat into a stadium, you're playing .... (8)
9 What a(n) ... ! That's 3-0 to Portugal! (4)

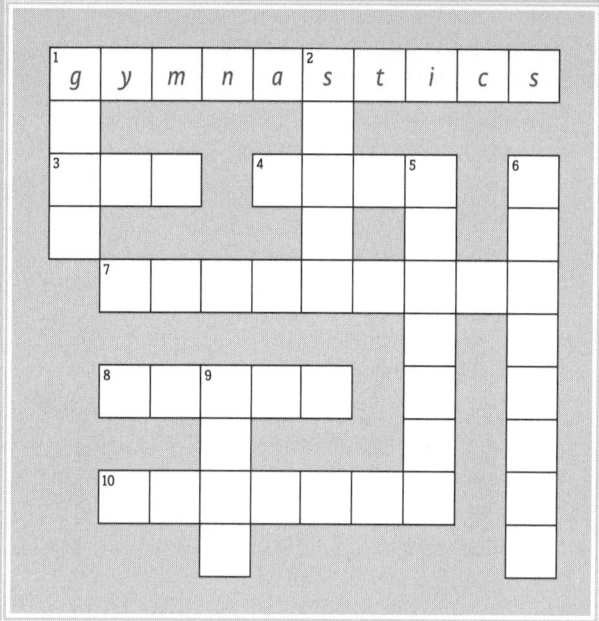

I CAN...

Reading

☐ I can understand an article about adventure courses.
☐ I can understand a magazine article about an extreme sport.

Vocabulary

☐ I can talk about sports, sports venues and equipment.

Grammar

☐ I can use the present continuous to talk about activities in progress and temporary situations.
☐ I can differentiate between present continuous and simple.
☐ I can use state verbs.

Listening

☐ I can understand an interview about a new extreme sport.
☐ I can understand a short sporting commentary.

Interaction

☐ I can understand a conversation asking for information.
☐ I can ask for information on the phone.

Challenge

☐ I can describe a picture and identify differences.

Writing

☐ I can use correct punctuation.
☐ I can write a description of a sport.

ERROR CORRECTION

1 *Sarah does swimming at the pool in summer.*
Sarah goes swimming at the pool in summer.
2 *Miranda watching the tennis on TV.*
3 *Thierry is usually playing volleyball on Tuesdays.*
4 *'Are you listening?' 'Yes, I do.'*
5 *Do you know the football court near my house?*
6 *You can use my hockey bat if you want.*
7 *I like to ask for some information.*
8 *Sam isn't here in the moment.*

Review Unit 3

CROSSWORD

Across

3 Are there ... cookies in the jar? (3)
4 Some people in India don't eat ... because of their respect for cows. (4)
6 Many people cry when they cut ... . (6)
9 You normally put the ... to the left of the plate and the knife to the right. (4)
11 Can I help you? What ... you like?(5)
12 'Have you got anything to eat?' 'We've got ... olives.'(4)

Down

1 First you spread some butter on the ... . (5)
2 Here, have a(n) ... so you don't get food on your clothes. (6)
5 To make 1 down, you need water, salt and ... . (5)
7 Would you like a(n) ... of cheese on your sandwich? (5)
8 The salad is better if you put a(n) ... tomatoes in it. (3)
10 Most Mediterranean countries use olive ... in cooking. (3)

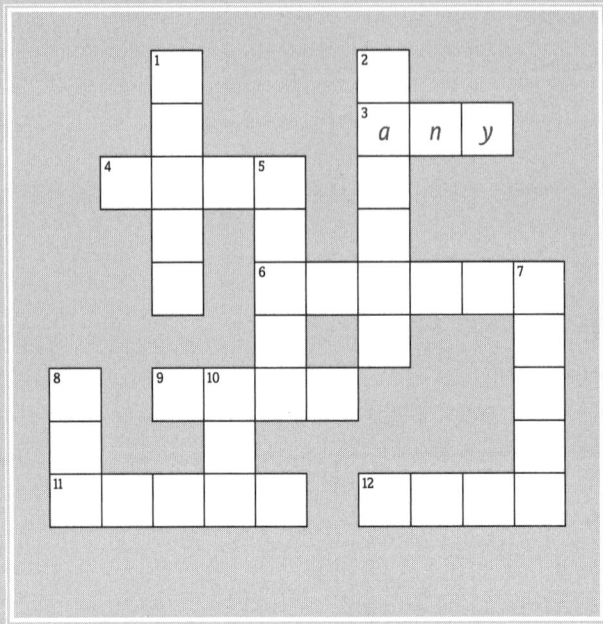

I CAN...

Reading

☐ I can understand an article about eating habits in different countries and an article reviewing restaurants.

Vocabulary

☐ I can talk about food and things you find at the table.
☐ I can identify different containers and portions.

Grammar

☐ I can use countable and uncountable nouns.
☐ I can use *some*, *any* and *no*.
☐ I can use various quantifiers.

Listening

☐ I can understand an excerpt from a cooking programme.

Interaction

☐ I can understand a conversation in a sandwich bar.
☐ I can order food and drink in a sandwich bar.

Challenge

☐ I can plan a meal with a friend.

Writing

☐ I can use expressions of time.
☐ I can write an article about my eating habits.

ERROR CORRECTION

1 *Do you want a bread with your soup?*
Do you want some bread with your soup?

2 *We haven't got no milk in the fridge.*

____

3 *Granddad sometimes has a cup of wine with dinner.*

____

4 *Get me a carton of mineral water from the shop.*

____

5 *How many homework does your teacher give?*

____

6 *'Is there any cheese?' 'Yes, there's a lot of.'*

____

7 *'How many is that?' 'That's €5.'*

____

8 *'Anything more?' 'Yes, I'd also like two coffees.'*

____

Review Unit 4

CROSSWORD

Across

2 They waved goodbye as they drove ... from the house.(4)
4 We didn't get the express train so we ... at every station. (7)
6 Then we climbed ... to the top of Picos de Europa. It was great! (2)
9 I can't hear you very well – I'm ... the train. (2)
10 We took Dad's car and ... around the island. (5)
12 Have you got a single ticket or a(n) ...? (6)

Down

1 A(n) ... is like a bike with a motor. (5)
2 They didn't like the food there so they ... hamburgers almost every day. (3)
3 A(n) ... is approximately 1.1 metres. (4)
4 His grandparents migrated to Australia from England by .... (4)
5 ... you have a good trip to Sicily? (3)
6 The boat trip was fun. We went ... all the bridges of the Seine. (5)
7 There was no bus service to the beach so we went on .... (4)
8 Third person plural of the verb *to be* in past simple affirmative: they .... (4)
11 You get ... the bus at the last stop and walk to the shops from there. (3)

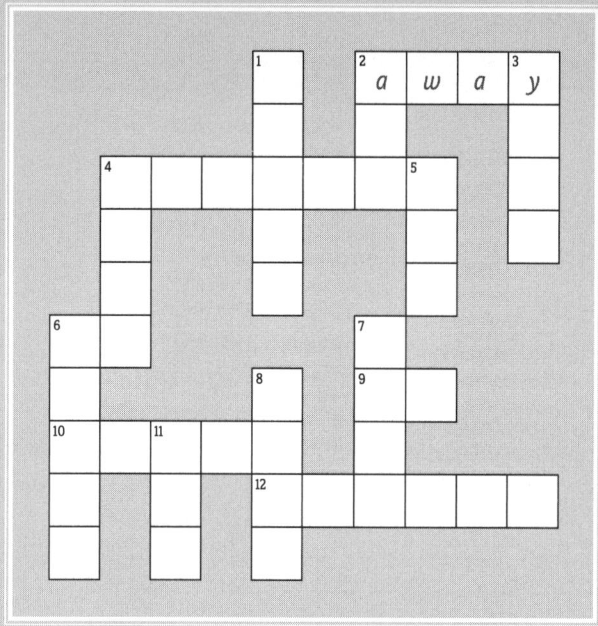

I CAN...

Reading

☐ I can understand a blog about a trip to a different country.
☐ I can understand an article about a famous voyage.

Vocabulary

☐ I can talk about transport.
☐ I can use prepositions of movement.

Grammar

☐ I can use the past simple affirmative.
☐ I can use *was* and *were*.
☐ I can form negative sentences and questions in the past simple.

Listening

☐ I can understand someone telling the story of a journey.

Interaction

☐ I can understand conversations on a bus and at a train station.
☐ I can buy tickets and ask for travel information.

Challenge

☐ I can describe a journey.

Writing

☐ I can use sequencing words and expressions.
☐ I can write a holiday blog.

ERROR CORRECTION

1 *James said goodbye and got on the taxi.*
James said goodbye and got into the taxi.

2 *My family went to Portugal in coach.*

____

3 *His mother drived him to school last year.*

____

4 *We was late because of the bus.*

____

5 *Shelley didn't walked home yesterday.*

____

6 *Did Charlie went with you?.*

____

7 *The ferry left ago ten minutes.*

____

8 *How long time does it take to get there?*

____

Review Unit 5

CROSSWORD

Across

1 I live in a rural area with lots of... . (8)
4 And you can learn to write your name in Chinese. That ... cool! (6)
6 The summers in the north of Scandinavia are ... . (5)
10 Mont Blanc is higher ... Mount Teide. (4)
12 The opposite of 6 across is ... . (4)
13 A(n) ... is a period of ten years. (6)

Down

2 Saturn is big, but not as big ... Jupiter. (2)
3 She is the ... intelligent person in our class. (4)
5 James, you're ... – can you help me move this box? (6)
6 We leave the butter out of the fridge so it's nice and ... – then it's easier to spread. (4)
7 Sorry we don't have any more T-shirts. We've sold ... . (3)
8 Then it started to rain and we got really ... . (3)
9 The Andes is the longest mountain ... on land. (5)
11 ... is the opposite of 6 down. (4)

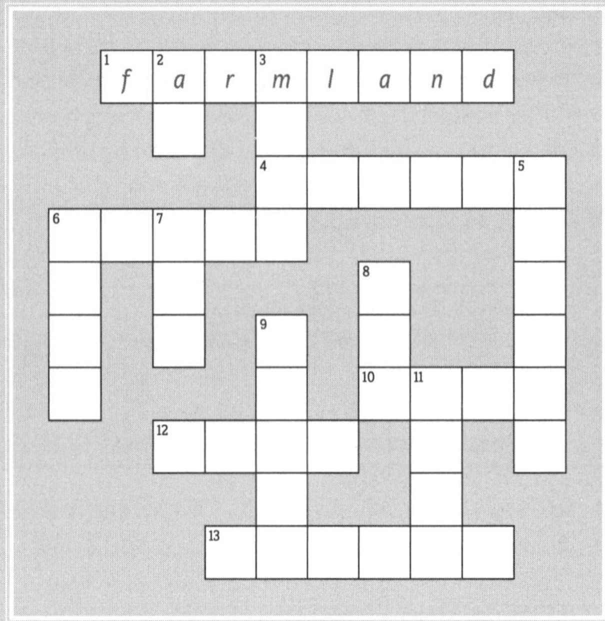

I CAN...

Reading

☐ I can understand a text about the Solar System.
☐ I can understand an article about the natural world.

Vocabulary

☐ I can use various adjectives and their opposites.
☐ I can talk about landscapes.

Grammar

☐ I can use comparatives.
☐ I can use *not as ... as* and *less*.
☐ I can use superlatives.
☐ I can use *the least*.

Listening

☐ I can understand a conversation about different museums.

Interaction

☐ I can understand a conversation in a museum gift shop.
☐ I can buy things in a gift shop.

Challenge

☐ I can work in a group to solve a problem.

Writing

☐ I can give examples and introduce lists.
☐ I can write a description of a landscape.

ERROR CORRECTION

1 *Careful jumping there! The water is very little deep.*
Careful jumping there! The water is very shallow.

2 *Uranus is very far from the Sun but Neptune is more far.*
____

3 *Canada is bigger that Australia.*
____

4 *Hockey isn't as exciting how rugby.*
____

5 *Sally is the more intelligent student in our class.*
____

6 *The test was least difficult than I thought.*
____

7 *I'd like one of that fridge magnets, please.*
____

8 *I'm sorry, we've sold of maps. They're very popular.*
____

Review Unit 6

CROSSWORD

Across

4 A weekend learning to kitesurf? That sounds ... ! (3)
5 ... it raining when you arrived? (3)
6 The ... put the perfume into her bag and walked out without paying. (10)
7 'What colour was the jacket?' 'I'm not ... . Blue, I think'(4)
9 My uncle once caught a(n) ... trying to rob his house. Thankfully he ran away without taking anything. (7)

Down

1 They stole her bag and her mobile phone. She was very ... . (5)
2 They broke ... the office and stole some important documents. (4)
3 A(n) ... is someone who steals cars and drives them for fun. (8)
5 ... he was talking to me, he put his hand in my pocket. (5)
6 Mum is cooking fish. I can ... it from my room. (5)
8 Siobhan is a very ... person – I've never once seen her get angry or nervous. (4)

I CAN...

Reading

☐ I can understand a crime story.
☐ I can understand an article about different crimes.

Vocabulary

☐ I can talk about feelings and moods.
☐ I can talk about people in crime.

Grammar

☐ I can use the past continuous.
☐ I can differentiate the past simple and the past continuous.
☐ I can use *when* and *while*.

Listening

☐ I can understand a series of short interviews between police officers and witnesses.

Interaction

☐ I can understand a conversation about a weekend or holiday.
☐ I can participate in a conversation about a weekend or holiday.

Challenge

☐ I can interview suspects and solve a crime.

Writing

☐ I can use some past time expressions.
☐ I can write a crime story.

ERROR CORRECTION

1 *Can we go now? I'm boring.*
Can we go now? I'm bored.

2 *I'd like to have lunch soon. I'm very angry.*

3 *When you texted me, I was watch that new science programme.*

4 *Come closer. I don't see you.*

5 *The pickpocket broke into the house.*

6 *While Sheila was cooking dinner, she was hearing a strange noise outside.*

7 *Did it raining when you left the house?*

8 *'How was your weekend?' 'I spent a great time.'*

Review Unit 7

CROSSWORD

Across

1 And he gave you half of his lunch? That's very ... ! (8)
6 Cara likes R&B, but she can't ... hip-hop. (5)
8 I've never ... outside of Europe. (4)
9 ... long have you lived in London? (3)
11 I've got blond hair, but my sister's hair is ... brown. (4)
12 Joanna's really ... – she never does anything to help. (4)

Down

2 My brother and I try to help ... other with our homework. (4)
3 Have you ... read a whole book in English? (4)
4 ... hair is hair that has no curl. (8)
5 Sam doesn't like animals, but he is ... of his pet hamster. (4)
6 I've had this MP3 player ... last Christmas. (5)
7 Dad started losing his hair at 25 and now he's completely ... . (4)
8 My Maths teacher has a(n) ... and a moustache. (5)
10 If your hair is not very curly, it's ... . (4)

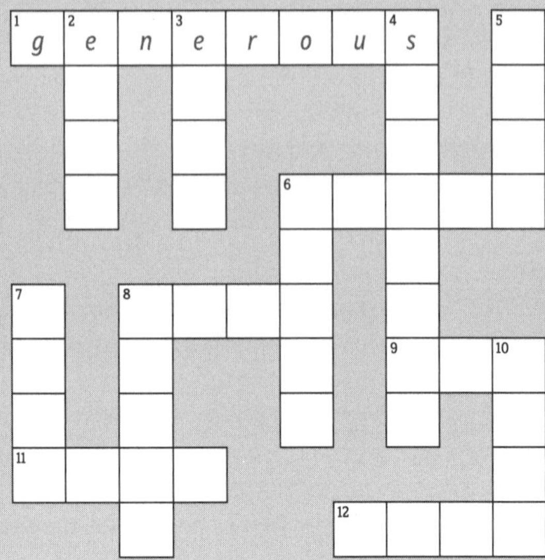

I CAN...

Reading

☐ I can understand an article about the interests of actors.
☐ I can understand an article about the qualities of best friends.

Vocabulary

☐ I can talk about skills and interests.
☐ I can describe people in character and appearance.

Grammar

☐ I can use the present perfect to talk about life experiences, the past and situations continuing in the present.
☐ I can use *ever*, *never*, *how long*, *for* and *since*.
☐ I can differentiate between *been* and *gone*.

Listening

☐ I can understand an interview with a rock band.

Interaction

☐ I can understand short conversations involving apologies.
☐ I can apologize and accept apologies.

Challenge

☐ I can find out about other people's experiences.

Writing

☐ I can use some referencing words.
☐ I can write an essay about a person I admire.

ERROR CORRECTION

1 *Paolo isn't very good in Maths.*
Paolo isn´t very good at Maths.

2 *She doesn't stand football.*
____

3 *Did you ever played Angry Birds?*
____

4 *We're best friends – we've known us for years.*
____

5 *She doesn't like meeting new people, she's very friendly.*
____

6 *Joan's lived in Wales since two years.*
____

7 *How long for have you had that mobile phone?*
____

8 *Joan's not here. She's been to the swimming pool.*
____

Review Unit 8

CROSSWORD

Across

4 When we come back from a weekend in the country, we always ... the car because it gets so dirty. (5)
7 I think my big sister will be a great ... representative. She's a very good talker! (5)
9 We take ... the rubbish every night after eight. (3)
10 What household chores do you ... to do? (4)
11 A(n) ... works with doctors and helps sick people. (5)

Down

1 After we ... the dog, we always take it for a walk. (4)
2 I want to be a(n) ... like my uncle, so I can tell people what to do! (7)
3 When the exam is finished, you ... put down your pens immediately. (4)
5 My mum does the washing, but my dad does his own ... – after all, they're his shirts! (7)
6 Are you ... to watch TV on weeknights? (7)
8 If you want to get better marks, you ... study harder! (6)

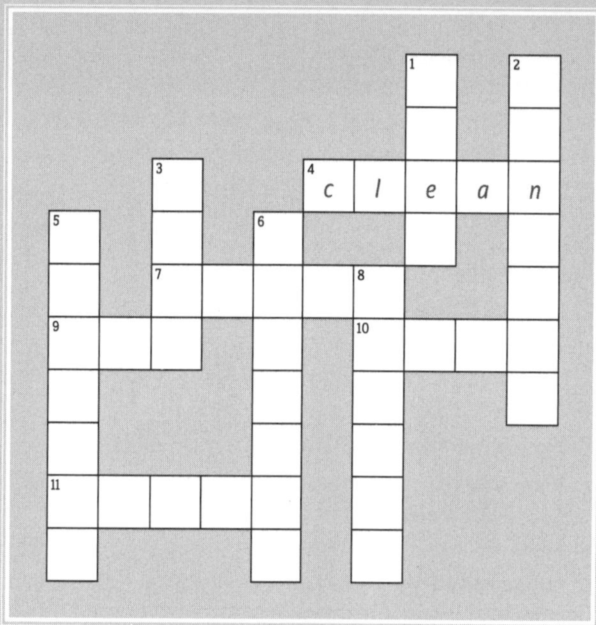

I CAN...

Reading

☐ I can understand an article about unusual jobs.
☐ I can understand an article about part-time jobs for teenagers.

Vocabulary

☐ I can talk about jobs.
☐ I can talk about household chores.

Grammar

☐ I can use modals for rules and obligation.
☐ I can use modals for permission, advice and suggestions.

Listening

☐ I can understand a TV game show about jobs.

Interaction

☐ I can understand conversations about problems and advice.
☐ I can understand problems and give advice.

Challenge

☐ I can do a job interview.

Writing

☐ I can use some adverbs.
☐ I can write an email about my school.

ERROR CORRECTION

1 *Meera's a nurse – she looks for sick people.*
Meera's a nurse – she looks after sick people.
2 *My Dad's an accountant. He designs buildings and houses.*
____
3 *At my school, we must to turn off our mobile phones in class.*
____
4 *I can't talk now. I have to take the dog walking.*
____
5 *Mum has done the shopping and now I have to take away the groceries.*
____
6 *My father has a new work.*
____
7 *Cheryl needs study harder if she wants to pass.*
____
8 *I'm not think that's a good idea.*
____

Review Unit 9

CROSSWORD

Across

1 The ... is working, but you need to put some more paper in it. (7)
5 Have you seen the new shopping ... in town? It's enormous! (6)
6 On Sundays we sometimes go to have a picnic in the .... (4)
10 The town ... is a beautiful building in the main square. (4)
11 So come to our farewell party. You won't ... it! (6)

Down

2 ... I can't come, I'll tell you. (2)
3 For my birthday, my family went out for dinner at my favourite .... (10)
4 If you need to send an email on holiday, you can look for an internet .... (4)
6 We just bought a Blu-ray disc .... It's awesome! (6)
7 This computer comes with a multi-card ... to import photos from any camera. (6)
8 When I finish school, I'm ... to travel round the world. (5)
9 I think tomorrow the weather ... be better. (4)

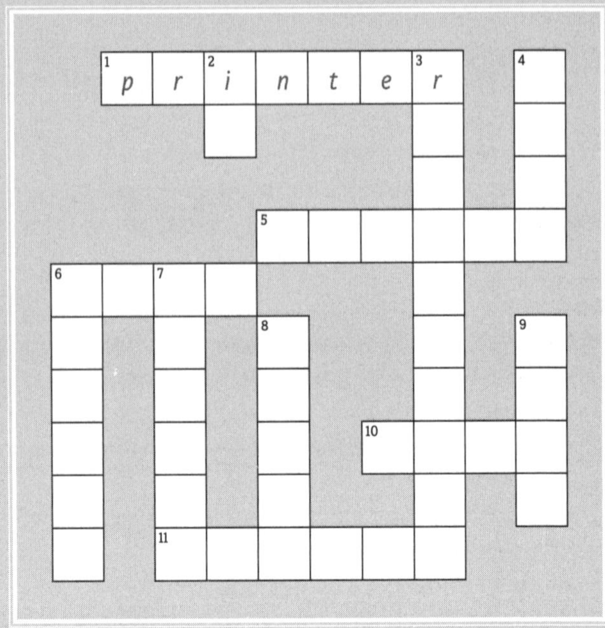

I CAN...

Reading

☐ I can understand an article about free-time activities in town and home entertainment in the past, present and future.

Vocabulary

☐ I can talk about places in a town.
☐ I can talk about digital entertainment.

Grammar

☐ I can use the present continuous and *be going to* for future plans and intentions.
☐ I can use *will* for predictions and first conditional sentences.

Listening

☐ I can understand a radio programme about a carnival.

Interaction

☐ I can understand conversations involving asking for and giving directions.
☐ I can ask for and give directions.

Challenge

☐ I can talk about a range of topics.

Writing

☐ I can report statistics.
☐ I can write a summary report.

ERROR CORRECTION

1 *I'm going down to the newsagent's to get some aspirin.*
I'm going down to the pharmacy to get some aspirin.

2 *Lisa went to the library to buy the last Harry Potter book.*

____

3 *Jeff goes to the sports centre one time a week.*

____

4 *'What are you doing this weekend?' 'I'll visit my grandparents.'*

____

5 *What do you going to do when you grow up?*

____

6 *We just bought a new home entertain system.*

____

7 *I won't go to go to school if it snows.*

____

8 *You can store all your digital photographs on your computer printer.*

____

A personal description

INTERPAL | SEARCH | FORUMS | CHAT

Start an informal message with *Hi* or *Hello*.

Hi everyone!

Use contractions in an informal message.

My name's Hanna and I'm from Denmark. I'm 13 years old and I live in Copenhagen with my parents. I haven't got any brothers or sisters.

Use *so* to introduce the reason for doing something.

Use adverbs of frequency to say how often you do something. NB Put adverbs of frequency before the main verb, but after *be*.

My school is near my house so I usually walk there with my friends. My favourite subjects are Drama and Art. I also like English, but I don't like Maths or Science.

Use *once / twice a week / month* to say how often you do something. NB use this expression at the beginning or end of a sentence.

Use *and* to list ideas in an affirmative sentences.

My favourite hobby is dancing. I have classes twice a week and I practise every day. I sometimes enter competitions and occasionally I win!

Use *or* to list ideas in a negative sentence.

Use *but* to connect two contrasting ideas.

In my free time, I like shopping and going out with my friends. I spend a lot of time on the computer but I don't watch TV very often. I don't play an instrument, or sing, but I love listening to music.

End your message with this phrase.

I would love to chat to people from all over the world, so please send me a message soon!

Hanna

Tips for writing English

We use a capital letter for nationalities, e.g.

He's Polish.
A Spanish omelette.
I've got a French pen friend.

For school subjects, we use a capital letter for languages (*English, Spanish*) and abbreviations (*ICT = information and computer technology, PE = physical education*), e.g.

I love English.
I think German is difficult.
We have PE lessons twice a week.

BUT

I don't like art.

A description of a sport

SEPAK TAKRAW

Sepak takraw is a fast, exciting sport. It's a combination of volleyball, football and gymnastics. It's popular in Southeast Asia, and it's Malaysia's national sport. The name comes from two languages. Sepak means 'kick' in Malay and takraw means 'ball' in Thai. People in Europe, Canada and the USA are starting to play it too.

The rules of sepak takraw are simple. Each team has three people on the court. They can use any part of their body, except their hands, to hit the ball over the net. They win a point if the other team can't hit it back to them. The sport's most famous competition is the King's Cup World Championship. It's on every year in Thailand, in August or September.

Sepak takraw is amazing to watch. In this photo, the player is flying through the air. He is trying to kick the ball over the net. There's more information and videos about it online.

Use a full stop at the end of a sentence.

Use an apostrophe to show possession, e.g. *the national sport of Malaysia = Malaysia's national sport.*

Use a capital letter at the beginning of a sentence.

Use a capital letter for the name of an event, e.g. *the French Open, the Olympics.*

Use a comma to separate different parts of a sentence.

[ ] In the third paragraph, give your opinion of the sport. If you've got a picture of the sport, describe what's happening in it.

Use an apostrophe in contractions, e.g. *It is = It's, They are = They're*

Use a comma to separate items in a list.

[ ] In the first paragraph, describe the sport and where it is played.

Use a capital letter for countries, months of the year and days of the week.

[ ] In the second paragraph, describe the rules. Mention any tournaments / championships and when they take place.

Tips for writing English

We use quotation marks ('...' or "...") around a word or phrase that is special in some way, e.g.

Sepak means 'kick' in Malay, and takraw means 'ball' in Thai.

We use quotation marks around the name of a book or film, e.g.

There's some information in a book called 'Unusual Sports'.

'Invictus' is a film about the 1995 Rugby World Cup in South Africa.

We use quotation marks around direct speech, e.g.

'It's a fantastic sport to play,' said a sepak takraw player.

'What are the rules of sepak takraw?' I asked.

A magazine article

What I eat

by Josh Harper, aged 13

[I'm not very hungry in the morning, so breakfast isn't my favourite meal. Before school, I have a small bowl of cereal or a piece of toast and a glass of orange juice. At the weekend, my mum cooks bacon and eggs.]

The school canteen is good. At lunchtime, they sell hot meals, sandwiches, salads and desserts, like apple pie or ice cream. The best thing is the pasta bar. Every week, they have a different sauce. This week it's chilli. After lunch, I have a cake or some fruit for dessert.

After school, I'm always really hungry. So before I do my homework, I have a cup of tea and some biscuits. We have dinner at seven in the evening. My favourite foods are roast chicken, curry and pizza. On Friday, we always have fish. I don't really like vegetables but I eat a lot of fruit.

Use *in* with *the morning*, *the afternoon* or *the evening*. NB We say *at night*.

Use *at* with *the weekend*. NB We can also say *at weekends*.

Use *at* with *lunchtime*. NB *lunchtime* is one word, but *breakfast time* and *dinner time* are two words.

Use *at* with times, e.g. *at midday*, *at 10.15 a.m.*, *at six o'clock*.

Use *before* or *after* before a noun like *school*, *breakfast*, *lunch* or *dinner*. NB We don't use an article with the noun, e.g. *after school* NOT ~~after the school~~.

[ ] Describe the food in chronological order, e.g. breakfast, lunch and then dinner.

Use *on* with days of the week. NB We can also say *on Fridays*, *on Wednesdays*.

Tips for writing English

We use *in* with *the morning* BUT if we say which day of the week, we use *on*, e.g.

on Monday morning, on Thursday evenings, on Saturday afternoons.

With clock times, we usually write numbers as words when followed by *o'clock* or when we don't use am or pm, e.g.

at nine o'clock, at eleven, at three.

However, we usually use numerals with am or pm, e.g. *at 7.15am, at 6.45pm.*

NB We say *at midday* and *at midnight* and not *at 12.00am* or *12.00pm.*

Writing Reference Unit 4

A holiday blog

Use *by* to introduce the author of a piece of writing.

Use *Then* for a second action. NB We can also say *Next*.

Sequencing words and expression are usually followed by a comma.

We use *Finally* for the last action.

A blog

by Anna Milton

Day 1

We arrived at our campsite at 10.00am after a 14-hour coach trip. First, we checked in at the campsite reception. Then we put up our tents. After that, we were all very tired and hungry. We had lunch and then we went to sleep for two hours. In the afternoon, we explored the campsite. The facilities on the campsite were good. There was a shop, a kitchen and a dining hall. There was also a great swimming pool, and the views of the mountains were amazing!

Day 5

Our last day! We got up early because we had a lot to do. First, we had breakfast. Then we started packing. It took me a long time to find all my things! After that, we took the tents down. Our tent was really dirty on the bottom so we needed to wash it before we put it away. Finally, we put everything into the back of the minibus and drove away. The journey home was OK but it took 20 hours instead of 14!

Use *First* for the first action. NB We can also say *First of all*.

Use *After that* for a subsequent action.

Use *and then* to describe a second action within one sentence.

[ ] When you write a blog about a holiday or a day trip, always use sequencing words and expressions so the reader knows the order of events.

Tips for writing English

In a piece of informal writing such as a blog, you can sometimes use an exclamation mark (!) instead of a full stop. We use exclamation marks to:

- make an exclamation, e.g. *What a fantastic trip! How amazing!*
- convey a strong feeling or opinion, e.g. *The views of the mountains were amazing! I love travelling!*
- convey a surprising fact, e.g. *It took 30 hours instead of 24!*

BUT remember!

Don't use exclamation marks in formal writing.

Don't use exclamation marks after every sentence.

Don't use more than one exclamation mark after a sentence, e.g. *What a great day!* NOT *What a great day!!!*

A description of a region

The Lake District

The Lake District is in Northwest England. It is the largest National Park in the country. It has its highest mountains and deepest lakes. It also has some of the most beautiful villages in Britain, such as Grasmere and Coniston. About 8 million people visit the Lake District every year.

Windermere is 17 km long and is England's largest lake. There are two busy towns near the lake: Ambleside to the north and Bowness to the east. These have many cafés, restaurants and shops. Windermere is a popular place for activities such as sailing, walking and fishing.

At 978 m, Scafell Pike is England's highest mountain. You do not need special equipment to climb it, but you need to be fit and strong. Other mountains, for example, Skiddaw (just north of Derwent Water), are easier to climb.

There is a variety of accommodation in the Lake District, including hotels, guesthouses, campsites and youth hostels. It rains a lot in the Lake District, so youth hostels are a better choice than campsites. They are not as expensive as hotels and guesthouses, but are often in very beautiful places.

Use the full form of the verbs in formal writing.

Use *such as* to introduce examples of what you are talking about, e.g. beautiful villages.

[ ] In the first paragraph, describe the location of the place and what it is like.

[ ] In subsequent paragraphs, describe the things you can see and do there.

Use *for example* to introduce an example of what you are talking about, e.g. mountains.

Use *including* to introduce examples of what you are talking about, e.g. types of accommodation.

Tips for writing English

We write the following points of the compass with a hyphen, *north-east, north-west, south-east, south-west.*

We usually use lower case letters for compass points, e.g.

Manchester is in the north-west of England.

I live on the south-east coast.

The abbreviation for kilometres is km, e.g. *Windermere is 17 km long.* NOT ~~*Windermere is 17 kms long.*~~

The abbreviation for metres is m, e.g. *At 978 m, ...* NOT ~~*At 978 ms*~~, ...

NB We usually use a comma in a four-digit number or larger, e.g. *At 1,098 m, ...*

Use numerals for statistics, e.g. *About 8 million people visit the Lake District every year.*

BUT

You can't start a sentence with a numeral. Write the number as a word, e.g.

Eight million people ... NOT ~~*8 million people ...*~~

A story

Kidnap!

[Last Saturday morning, Ravi was the only one at home. His parents were out shopping and his sister was visiting a friend. Smiling happily, he made himself some toast and jam. Five minutes later, he sat down on the sofa to eat it.]

[Suddenly, he heard a loud noise coming from the street outside. He jumped up and opened the blinds. He couldn't believe his eyes! A man was grabbing a girl and pulling her into a car. She was kicking and screaming but no one was helping her.

Ravi quickly phoned the police. Then he ran downstairs. But when he got there, he noticed something strange. All his neighbours were in the street, but they didn't look worried or frightened. They were laughing and joking and looked happy.]

[Ravi pushed his way to the front of the crowd, and in the end, understood what was happening. There were no kidnappers in his street. They were actors making a film. Just then he heard the police car arrive. Feeling very embarrassed, he went over to explain his mistake.]

Use past time expressions to say when the story / the events happened.

[ ] In the first paragraph, set the scene for the story.

Use the past simple for finished actions.

Use the past continuous for background descriptions.

Use this expression before you describe something dramatic that was happening. NB The possessive adjective changes if the subject pronoun changes, e.g. I couldn't believe my eyes! They couldn't believe their eyes!

[ ] In the second and third paragraphs, write about the subsequent events.

[ ] In the final paragraph, describe how the story ended.

Tips for writing English

We use adverbs in stories to make our writing more interesting, e.g.

Smiling happily, he ...
Suddenly he heard a loud noise.
Ravi quickly phoned the police.

If an adjective ends in *ly*, we can't add *ly* to make an adverb. Instead, we use an adverb phrase, e.g

friendly – She looked at me in a friendly way.
silly – The boy behaved in a silly manner.

An essay

Use an object pronoun to refer to the person you mentioned before, rather than repeat their name. Use *him* for a male, *her* for a female and *them* for two or more people.

[ ] In the first paragraph, introduce the person and their relationship to you. You can write about the person's appearance and personality here.

Use a demonstrative pronoun to refer to someone / something you mentioned before.

Use the object pronoun *it* to refer to something you mentioned before, rather than repeat its name.

A person I admire

[A person that I admire a lot is my cousin James. He's a few years older than me but we get on really well. I've known him since I was six years old. That's when he moved to Britain from Australia. I've never been there, but I hope to go when I'm older.]

[James is really into music. He plays the guitar, and has just joined a band. They're called Strangers and have already played a couple of gigs. He listens to music all the time, especially Fleet Foxes and Mumford & Sons. Those are definitely his favourite bands at the moment.]

[James did a lot of sport when he was in Australia and he still loves it now. He plays cricket for his school team and is a member of a tennis club. He likes football as well, and supports Arsenal. We've been to see them play at the Emirates stadium a couple of times and we always watch them on TV.]

[These are just a few of the reasons why I admire James. He's a cheerful and generous person and it's fun to be with him.]

Use a subject pronoun to refer to the person you mentioned in the previous sentence, rather than repeat their name. Use *he* for a male, *she* for a female and *they* for two or more people.

Use *there* to refer to a place you mentioned before, rather than repeat the name.

[ ] In the second and third paragraphs, write about the person's interests, hobbies and achievements.

[ ] In the final paragraph, summarize why you admire the person.

Tips for writing English

In informal writing, we sometimes omit the second subject pronoun in a sentence if it is the same as the first, e.g.

He plays the guitar and ~~he~~ has just joined a band.

We've been to see them play and ~~we~~ always watch them on TV.

We have to include the second subject pronoun if it is different from the first, e.g.

I'm friends with James and he supports Arsenal. NOT ~~*I'm friends with James and supports Arsenal.*~~

An email about school rules

Write the name of the person you're emailing here.

Write the subject of the email here.

Use *really* to add emphasis.

Use this informal way to introduce information about something / someone.

Use *just* here to mean a *very short time*.

Use *instead* when you explain what you can do in place of something else.

You can use *almost* here too.

Use this sentence to finish your email. It means that you don't mind answering any questions about the topic.

To: Alicia
From: Melissa
Subject: My school

Hi Alicia,

I'm really looking forward to your visit. I hope you'll enjoy coming to my school with me.

[Let me tell you a bit about my school. It's called Seabrooke Academy, and it has almost 1000 students. We don't have to wear a school uniform but we aren't allowed to wear jeans. We live near to the school so we don't have to catch a bus. We have to be in school by 8.35am every day for registration, and we finish at 3.00pm.

Lunch is just before 12.15. We have quite a nice canteen, but you don't have to eat there. You can bring a packed lunch instead if you prefer. We only have half an hour for lunch so we have to eat quickly!

Our facilities are very good, especially our sports centre. It even has a swimming pool we can use! There's also a music block. I have to do guitar practice there nearly every day after school.]

If you need to know anything else about my school, just ask. I'm looking forward to meeting you!

See you soon,
Melissa

Write your name here.

Start an informal email with *Hi* or *Dear* and the person's first name.

Use contractions in an informal email.

Use *almost* to mean *just under* a number. You can also use *nearly* here.

Use *quite* to convey to a certain degree.

Use *especially* to emphasize an example.

Use *also* to introduce another example.

[ ] In the main part of the email, give interesting bits of information about the topic.

Tips for writing English

We use a meaningful subject to describe the content of the message, e.g.

Subject: My school

We use an appropriate salutation before we jump into the text, e.g.

I'm really looking forward to your visit. I hope you'll enjoy coming to my school with me.

A report

[ ] In paragraph 1, explain who you spoke to and why.

Use expressions like these to report your statistics.

My report

A [For this report, I spoke to 16 people in my class. I asked them about their favourite free-time activities and about what they are doing this weekend.]

B [About half of the people I spoke to like doing sport in their free time. Some of them play football and others go swimming. 8 people have classes outside school. 2 of them go to drama classes and 5 are learning to play an instrument. Only 1 student does Karate.]

C Almost all the students in my class spend a lot of time on the computer. Most of them spend over 2 hours a day playing games or social network sites. Everyone uses the computer to do their homework.

D About 80% of the students in my class have plans for the weekend. 11 people are meeting up with friends. 2 of those are going to the cinema and 3 others are going ice-skating. No one is going to a theatre, art gallery or museum this weekend.

E [It was interesting to learn how much time people in this class spend on the computer. Perhaps we should all do a bit more sport instead, or visit museums more often.]

Use the full form of verbs in a formal report.

Use this structure to report your statistics.

[ ] In subsequent paragraphs, write the results of your survey. Use a separate paragraph for each topic.

Use indefinite pronouns to report your statistics.

Use this expression to make a suggestion

[ ] In the last paragraph, give your opinion on the results.

Tips for writing English

We usually write small numbers up to twenty as words, e.g.

I asked three people about music. NOT ~~I asked 3 people about music.~~

There were nine people in the room. NOT ~~There were 9 people in the room.~~

We usually write numbers over twenty as numerals, e.g.

I spoke to 25 students. NOT ~~I spoke to twenty five students.~~

We usually write percentages as a numeral and a percentage sign, e.g.

About 80% of the students ... NOT ~~About eighty percent of the students ...~~

But write the percentage as words if it starts the sentence, e.g.

Ten percent of people ... NOT ~~10% of people ...~~

SPEAKING Giving personal information

Look again at page 122 of your Student's Book. Read *About the exam* and the *Tip*. Then do the task below.

Read the examiner's questions 1–7 and write your own answers.

1 What's your surname?

____

2 How do you spell it?

____

3 Where do you come from?

____

4 Tell me about your home.

____

____

____

5 Do you study English at school?

____

6 What do you enjoy doing in your free time?

____

____

____

7 Tell me about your family.

____

____

____

Prepare for the TOEFL Junior® Test Unit 1

LISTENING COMPREHENSION Classroom instruction

Look again at page 123 of your Student's Book. Read *About the test* and the *Tip*. Then do the task below.

29 Listen to four different teachers talking to students. For each question, mark the correct letter A, B, C, or D.

1 What is the teacher explaining?
A how to represent data
B how to do everyday activities
C how to record data
D how to write a questionnaire

2 What is the purpose of the teacher's announcement?
A to explain Nobel Prizes
B to find out about the Curie family
C to explain the homework
D to help students copy information

3 What is the purpose of the teacher's announcement?
A to introduce a new member of the class
B to encourage people to learn languages
C to tell people to travel more
D to find out about the new student

4 What is the subject of the announcement?
A the school trip to Argentina
B the things they need to take on their school trip
C who they will greet when they arrive in Argentina
D what they will do in class to prepare for the trip

WRITING Writing a letter

Look again at page 124 of your Student's Book. Read the *About the exam* and the *Tip*. Then do the task below.

This is part of a letter you receive from a British friend, Max.
Write a letter answering your friend's questions.
Write about **100 words**.

We're watching the Olympics at the moment! It's so exciting! Luckily, we've got two TVs at home. Mum and Dad are watching athletics in the living room. My brother and I are in the kitchen watching mountain biking. That's my favourite. I go mountain biking a lot, but I always wear a helmet. It can be quite dangerous! What about you? What's your favourite sport? Do you do any sports at school or as a hobby? Are you watching the Olympics? What do you and your family like to watch best?

WRITING Email

Look again at page 125 of your Student's Book. Read *About the test* and the *Tip*. Then do the task below.

Read the email and write a reply. Remember to answer all the questions.

From: Mickey
To: Class 8B
Subject: End-of-year outing

Dear classmates,

I'm organizing the end-of-year outing, which will take place on March 22nd. Last year we all enjoyed our trip to the science museum. This year, I thought it would be good to do something active.

Would you like to play a sport outside or inside? Why?

Would you prefer to play a team sport or an individual sport? Why?

Finally, think of where you would like to eat afterwards. We can choose between Italian or Chinese.

Please reply by the end of the week.

Best wishes

Mickey

SPEAKING Describing a photo

Look again at page 126 of your Student's Book. Read *About the exam* and the *Tip*. Then do task 1 below.

1 Choose one of the photos and write a description of it. Answer the following questions.

Where are the people?
What are they doing?
What are they wearing?
How are the people feeling?
What food and other objects can you see?

____

____

____

____

____

____

____

Taking turns and showing interest

Look again at page 126 of your Student's Book. Read *About the exam* and the *Tip*. Then do task 2 below.

2 Read the examiner's questions. Then read Student A's comments and write your responses according to the comments in brackets. Don't forget to use words and phrases to show interest and keep the conversation going.

Examiner: Your photographs showed people and food. Now I'd like you to talk together about the food you eat at home and the food you eat in restaurants.

Student A: I usually eat healthy food at home during the week. My parents do most of the cooking, but my sister and I have to help. We always eat a lot of vegetables and fish. What about you?

You: (Say what you eat at home during the week and who prepares it.)

____

____

Student A: At the weekend, I like making pizza. I know it isn't very healthy, but it's delicious. I put lots of cheese and meat on the pizza, and eat it with chips.

You: (Say what you usually eat at the weekend at home. Is it healthy? Ask Student A if they go to restaurants.)

____

____

Student A: Yes, we always go to a restaurant every Sunday. Do you?

You: (Answer Student A's question.)

____

____

Student A: Really? My parents like to go to restaurants where they cook traditional food with local ingredients. I like that too, but my favourite type of restaurant is Chinese. I love noodles! What about you?

You: (Answer Student A's question.)

____

____

Prepare for the TOEFL Junior® Test Unit 3

READING COMPREHENSION Narrative (story)

Look again at page 127 of your Student's Book. Read *About the test* and the *Tip*. Then do the task below.

Read the story. For each question, mark the correct letter A, B, C, or D.

It can be a strange feeling to be in another country – away from your home and all the things you know. Well, here I am with my host family, the Hellströms, in Stockholm on a student cultural exchange program. The Hellströms are a really friendly family, and they are organizing a welcome dinner tonight as it's my first day here. I'm wearing my nice blouse, since they all dress so well here.

The restaurant we're in is called Smörga. My host dad asks for a selection of Swedish food for me to taste – I hope I like it.

As a starter, we have some fish, which is very typical in Sweden. It's very nice, but fish isn't my favorite thing. There's also some delicious meat, which I eat a lot of.

"Do you know what kind of meat that is?" asks my host dad.

I shake my head, "No, it's delicious though." I reply.

"It's… How do you say it? You know, the animals that help Father Christmas …"

"Reindeer, you mean?" I'm quite surprised by this. The waiter laughs and so does my host family.

For the main course, there are some Swedish meatballs – they are famous around the world. I try some. My host mom says, "You can eat them with this, too." She passes me a plate of what looks like some sort of insects. They all look at me. Then I think the dad guesses what I'm thinking.

"It's OK. It's a type of pasta – not insects. Though tomorrow, we're planning a walk in the forest, so we can collect some insects to try!"

"That's OK," I reply. "I love pasta and reindeer!"

As we continue to eat, I learn something interesting. It is traditional in Sweden to talk to the person on your left when eating the starter, the people on your left and right for the main course, and the person opposite you for dessert.

As I pick up my fork to eat my apple pie, I talk to Anika, my exchange friend. We both agree, our favorite meal is a burger and French fries!

1 Why is the writer in Stockholm?

A to try the local food
B to learn about the culture
C to teach Swedish people how to cook
D to visit family and friends

2 In line 16, the word taste is closest in meaning to ______ .

A lick
B try
C look at
D find

3 In line 37, the word them refers to ______ .

A the host mom
B the insects
C the Swedish people
D the meatballs

4 According to the story, the writer likes the following food EXCEPT …

A reindeer
B pasta
C burgers
D insects

READING Choosing the correct option

Look again at page 128 of your Student's Book. Read *About the exam* and the *Tip*. Then do the task below.

Read the text. For each question, choose the correct letter A, B, C or D.

Example:

	A	B	C	D
0	**A** out	**B** on	**C** under	**D** over

Answer: B

See London in a 'Duck'

An unusual way to see London is to get **(0)** … a DUKW truck, also called a 'Duck'. The US army **(1)** … these amphibious trucks in the Second World War to move goods and soldiers **(2)** … land and water. They have six wheels and are shaped **(3)** … a boat, making **(4)** … equally good to drive on roads or to sail on rivers, lakes or even the sea. After the war, a man **(5)** … bought a DUKW at an auction in 1946 **(6)** … using them for 'Duck tours' in Wisconsin. Nowadays, you can still enjoy a tour **(7)** … the area on the Original Wisconsin Ducks and they are used in **(8)** … coastal or river cities around the world, **(9)** … the UK capital. Recently I went on a London Duck Tour with some friends. It **(10)** … for 75 minutes and we saw many of the sights, including Buckingham Palace and MI5, before we went for a sail on the river Thames.

	A	B	C	D
1	**A** used	**B** travelled	**C** moved	**D** saw
2	**A** under	**B** into	**C** along	**D** across
3	**A** for	**B** like	**C** how	**D** to
4	**A** they	**B** him	**C** them	**D** it
5	**A** which	**B** whose	**C** whom	**D** who
6	**A** started	**B** thought	**C** decided	**D** made
7	**A** around	**B** up	**C** between	**D** towards
8	**A** many	**B** much	**C** too	**D** very
9	**A** with	**B** but	**C** including	**D** by
10	**A** took	**B** happened	**C** longed	**D** lasted

LANGUAGE FORM AND MEANING

Look again at page 129 of your Student's Book. Read *About the test* and the *Tip*. Then do the task below.

Read the text and choose the best letters A, B, C, or D.

1. A team of extreme athletes recently [A went / B go / C been / D gone] to the Ecuadorian Amazon to complete an adventure race of almost 700 kilometers.

2. [A After that / B On / C At / D When] they had two stages left to complete, the four team

3. members met a dog and gave [A his / B him / C he / D them] some food.

4. The dog stayed with them [A before / B about / C during / D on] the race, even at the kayaking stage,

5. when they tried to leave him behind. The dog jumped [A into / B over / C up / D on to] the water and swam alongside them. The team decided to name the dog Arthur

6. and he [A played / B went / C finished / D took] the race as a fifth member of the team. Mikael, the team captain, decided to adopt Arthur and take him home.

SPEAKING Making suggestions, agreeing and disagreeing

Look again at page 130 of your Student's Book. Read *About the exam* and the *Tip*. Then do the task below.

Read the task and look at the pictures. Then read Student A's suggestions and write your responses according to the comments in brackets.

A science teacher is leaving his school to work in a different city. Some of his students want to give him a present. Talk together about the different presents they could give him and then decide which would be best.

Student A: It's a pity that Mr. Jones is leaving. He's a good science teacher. What do you think we should buy him as a leaving present?

You: [agree with student A; suggest a cake]

____

____

____

Student A: I'm not sure. I don't think he likes cakes. He never eats our birthday cakes!

You: [agree; suggest a photo of the class]

____

____

____

Student A: Maybe, but do you think he'll want to have a photo of his students at home? What about a present connected with science instead? How about a telescope? I think he's interested in the stars.

You: [disagree with the suggestion; give a reason why; suggest the book *A Brief History of Time* instead]

____

____

____

Student A: That's a good idea. I think he would like that. But do you think he might have it already? What about something practical – like a wall calendar.

You: [disagree with the suggestion; suggest a ticket to the science exhibition]

____

____

____

Student A: That's a great idea. How about buying two tickets, then he can invite someone to go with him.

You: [agree; suggest that you order them online]

____

____

____

LISTENING COMPREHENSION Short conversations

Look again at page 131 of your Student's Book. Read *About the test* and the *Tip*. Then do the tasks below.

1 (30) Listen to a conversation between two students at school and then answer questions 1-4.

1 **What are the students mainly talking about?**
A how quickly comets travel
B the picture of the probe landing
C how small the comet is
D if the probe landing really happened

2 **Why does one student think that the story is not true?**
A He saw the pictures of the landing.
B He heard the sound of the probe landing.
C He read articles saying it wasn't true.
D He thinks people always lie.

3 **What does the student mean when he says '*Yes, exactly.*'?**
A He's agreeing with the other boy's example of special effects.
B People should know what comets look like.
C The probe landed exactly in the right place.
D He's agreeing that the probe landing is true.

4 **What will the two boys probably do next?**
A Make up some stories about the comet.
B Go and watch a movie about space.
C Look for the stories about the probe landing.
D Find a picture of what comets look like.

2 (31) Listen to a conversation between a social science teacher and a student at school and then answer questions 5-8.

5 **What is the conversation mostly about?**
A Lucy's project
B the rain forests in South America
C the class presentations
D how to do research

6 **According to the conversation, Lucy thinks that _____ .**
A the cloud forest in Chile is in the Atacama Desert
B there aren't any cloud forests in other continents
C students are less interested in finding out things that they already know
D all students know about cloud forests

7 **Why does the teacher say she is lucky?**
A She's got a good memory.
B She's got some good students.
C She doesn't need to do the presentation.
D She had the chance to visit a cloud forest.

8 **According to the conversation, which of the following is NOT true?**
A There are temperate cloud forests in several Latin American countries.
B Lucy went to Fray Jorge National Park in Chile.
C Lucy is doing a presentation with other students.
D Ms. Gray is going to look for some photos of the Chilean Cloud Forest.

WRITING Writing a story from a first sentence

Look again at page 132 of your Student's Book. Read *About the exam* and the *Tip*. Then do the task below.

Read the task and write a story.

- Your English teacher has asked you to write a story.
- Your story must begin with this sentence:

It was the middle of the night when my sister came running into my room screaming.

Write your story in about **100 words**.

SPEAKING Picture narration

Look again at page 133 of your Student's Book. Read *About the test* and the *Tip*. Then do the task below.

Look at the picture story. Write the story below. You will have one minute to tell the story. That's about 10 seconds for each picture, so you would have time to say about two sentences for each picture. Look again at the words in the chart in exercise 2 on page 133 of your Student's Book to help you.

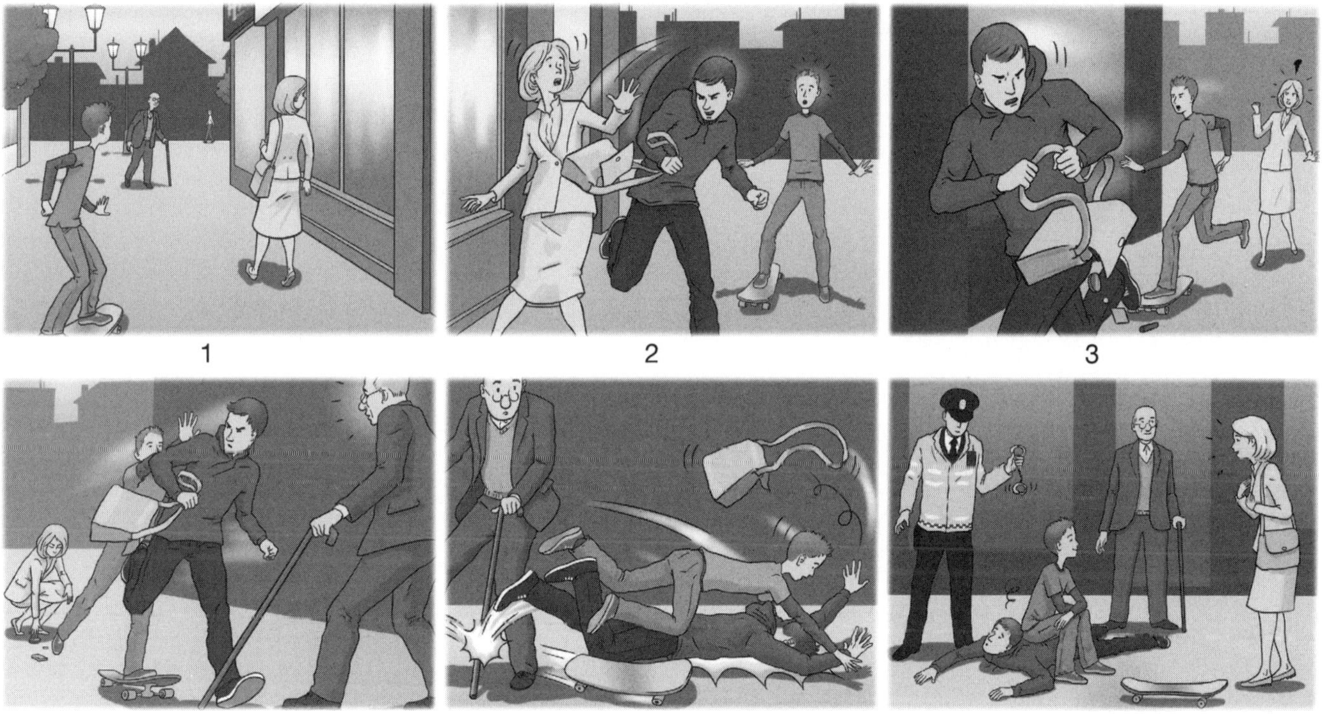

1 2 3

4 5 6

LISTENING Listening for specific information

32 Look again at page 134 of your Student's Book. Read *About the exam* and the *Tip*. Then do the task below.

You will hear someone talking about their three children.
For each question, choose the correct answer A, B or C.

1 Ruben was born in

A 1980.
B 1982.
C 1990.

2 Mollie

A is at university.
B is a baby.
C has completed her university education.

3 The speaker believes that

A children are all the same.
B all children are unique individuals.
C her children have similar abilities and interests.

4 Ewan

A is a quiet person who loves reading.
B is very cheerful.
C is keen on all sports.

5 Ruben

A is tall and thin.
B has got black hair and a beard.
C is strong and well-built.

6 Mollie

A plays the trumpet and the piano.
B has got curly red hair.
C has read a lot of novels.

Prepare for the TOEFL Junior® Test Unit 7

READING COMPREHENSION Announcement

Look again at page 135 of your Student's Book. Read *About the test* and the *Tip*. Then do the task below.

Read the announcement and answer questions 1-4.

Join the school movie club

When do we meet?
The movie club meets twice a week on Tuesdays and Thursdays after school.

Where do we meet?
We meet in H357.

Who can come?
All students are welcome – you simply need to be a fan of movies.

What do you watch?
We love watching all kinds of modern and classic movies of different genres and from a range of movie directors.

What else do you do?
We discuss the history of film, and techniques and technology used in movie making. We also debate specific movies.

How long has the club existed?
Believe it or not, the school has had a movie club for over 10 years!

How much does it cost?
It's free! Soft drinks and popcorn are also provided.

1 Who can join the movie club?
A all students who study in H357
B any student of any age
C students who go to clubs twice a week
D students who know about the history of films

2 In line 8, the word a fan is closest in meaning to _______ .
A an enthusiast
B a star
C a director
D an expert

3 In line 16, the word specific is closest in meaning to _______ .
A unusual
B peaceful
C horror
D particular

4 As well as watching movies, what other activities do they do?
A making movies
B making popcorn
C discussing movies
D classifying movies

READING Reading for detail and specific information

Look again at page 136 of your Student's Book. Read *About the exam* and the *Tip*. Then do the task below.

The people in the left column are all planning a holiday.
In the right column there are descriptions of eight holidays.
Decide which holiday would be most suitable for the following people.
Mark A – H for 1 – 5.

1 Annabelle is an architect who is really into historical buildings. She's very busy on a project so she shouldn't take too long off work – but she really needs a short break.

Holiday ____________

2 Julia spends her life flying all over the world. As a commercial pilot, she's used to taking other people on holiday, but all she wants for herself is to stay closer to home, relaxing with her family.

Holiday ____________

3 Tom's a plumber who is tired of being stuck indoors! He wants to take his girlfriend away for a couple of weeks. The accommodation must be clean and comfortable, but his budget is quite small.

Holiday ____________

4 Clare is a teacher at a primary school in London. It's the summer holidays, and time for a break – and an escape from noisy children! Clare's budget is from £600 – £1000, and she wants to go away with her friends.

Holiday ____________

5 Although Sam enjoys his work as an accountant, he sometimes needs a bit more excitement in his life! He has saved up enough money to take a few months off work, and is trying to decide what to do.

Holiday ____________

A
Come to Spain for sun, sand and sea! Two weeks for two in a beach-front apartment. It might not be the height of luxury, but it will offer you all the basic amenities you need at a price that's great for your pocket!

B
Do you want the ultimate in peace and quiet? If money is no object, you can hide away on your own island in the middle of nowhere. From a week to a month, the choice is yours…

C
'Staycations' are the new vacations! Why go to another country when your own country has everything you need for an amazing holiday? From traditional seaside resorts to wild, unspoiled beaches, the UK has wonderful places for adults and children alike.

D
Searching for adventure? Look no more! From scuba diving in the Great Barrier Reef to trekking on Mount Kilimanjaro, we can tailor-make the perfect holiday for you. Talk to us about what you're looking for… We know we can give you the answers you need!

E
Our all-inclusive deal offers you all you could ever want in a holiday. Free food, free drinks – and free fun! In our adult-only hotel, you can party all night and sleep all day!

F
Come to Prague for a weekend, and you will be sure to want to return – again and again! With its impressive architecture, vibrant art and music scene, and its plethora of restaurants, this city will stimulate all your senses and give you a wonderful escape.

G
Voluntary work abroad is like a holiday with a difference. You have a holiday from your normal life, and you make a real difference to the lives of people in need. Adults from 18 to 80 welcome to sign up. Minimum period one year.

H
Don't like getting wet, cold and soggy? Hate cooking on a tiny stove with few utensils? Love being in nature? Try 'glamping'! Glamorous camping in a heated yurt, with all meals provided. Try our taster one-night break – and see what you've been missing!

WRITING Opinion

Look again at page 137 of your Student's Book. Read *About the test* and the *Tip*. Then do the task below.

Read the task and write your essay. Remember to plan your essay carefully and use the useful phrases to organize your ideas and give your opinion.

Now you will write a paragraph expressing your opinion on a topic. You will have **10 minutes** to plan and write your response. Be sure to include reasons and examples to support your opinion. Write in complete sentences. When you are finished writing, check your response for grammar, spelling, and punctuation. Your paragraph should be between 100 and 150 words long.

All schools have rules, but are they necessary? Some people think that students should be capable of behaving well without any rules at all. Other people think that it is essential to have rules at school, so that students know what is expected of them. What do you think?

Prepare for Cambridge Exams Unit 9

WRITING Using grammar correctly

Look again at page 138 of your Student's Book. Read *About the exam* and the *Tip*. Then do the task below.

Here are some sentences about a family's computers.
For each question, complete the second sentence so that it means the same as the first. Use no more than three words.

1 My dad's computer is so ancient, it's got no USB ports!
My dad's computer is so ancient, it .... USB ports!

2 My sister uses her computer daily.
My sister uses her computer ....

3 My mum hasn't had a new computer for a long time.
It's a long time .... my mum had a new computer.

4 My computer is a bit faster than yours.
My computer is a .... faster than yours.

5 My brother's computer is less powerful than mine.
My brother's computer is not .... mine.

SPEAKING Read aloud

Look again at page 139 of your Student's Book. Read *About the test* and the *Tip*. Then do the tasks below.

1 33 Listen to and read three words that will appear in the passage.

celebrate
surprisingly
older

2 Now read the passage aloud.

Birthdays

Why are some birthdays so special to people and others are not? In some countries, people celebrate coming of age at 15 years old, whereas in other countries, people celebrate at 18 years old, and some people have to wait until they're 21. Surprisingly, in the Philippines, for girls their "debut" is at 18, but for boys, it's not until they're 21. As we get older, people tend to mainly celebrate round numbers – so forty, fifty, and sixty. After that, birthdays often become important every five years: sixty-five, seventy, and seventy-five. In my opinion, birthdays are fun, and so all of them should be celebrated. What do you think?

Vocabulary Bank

UNIT 1

aunt
brother
brush your teeth
children
cousin
dad
daughter
do sport
do the housework
do your homework
get dressed
get ready for bed
go online
go to school
go to the cinema
grandchildren
granddad
grandma
grandparents
great-grandparents
have a shower
have a snack
have breakfast
have dinner
have lunch
husband
meet friends
mum
nephew
nephew
niece
only child
sister
son
stepfather
stepmother
tidy your room
uncle
visit relatives
wife

UNIT 2

athletics
baseball
baseball bat
basketball
basketball net
climbing
do
elbow pads
football
football boots
football pitch
go
goal
gym
gymnastics
handball
helmet
hockey stick
horse riding
ice hockey
ice rink
ice skates
judo
kayak
kayaking
knee
mountain biking
paddle
play
rugby
running track
sailing
skate park
skateboarding
ski slope
skiing
skis
surfboard
surfing
swimming
swimming pool
tennis
tennis court
tennis racket
volleyball

UNIT 3

bag
beef
bottle
bowl
bread
butter

cabbage
can
carton
cheese
chicken
chopsticks
cucumber
cup
flour
fork
glass
grapes
green beans
jar
jug
knife
lemon
lettuce
milk
napkin
oil
onions
packet
pasta
peach
peas
peppers
piece
pineapple
plate
pork
prawns
rice
salmon
saucer
slice
spoon
strawberries
teaspoon
tomato
tuna
yoghurt

UNIT 4

across
along
around
away from
be on (the bus)
between
bike
bus
car
coach
down
ferry
go by (car)
go on foot
helicopter
horse
hot-air balloon
into
lorry
minibus
moped
motorbike
out of
plane
ship
taxi
through
towards
train
tram
under
underground
up
van
yacht

UNIT 5

beach
beautiful
boring
cheap
coastline
dangerous
deep
desert
dry
early
empty
expensive
far
farmland
fast
forest

full
hard
heavy
hill
interesting
island
lake
late
light
long
mountain
mountain ranges
narrow
near
noisy
plains
popular
quiet
river
safe
sea
shallow
short
slow
soft
stream
strong
thick
thin
ugly
unpopular
valley
volcano
weak
wet
wide

UNIT 6

angry
annoyed
bank robber
bored
burglar
calm
detective
embarrassed
excited
frightened
graffiti artist
hacker
happy
hungry
joyrider
judge
mugger
nervous
pickpocket
sad
shoplifter
thirsty
tired
upset
vandal
witness

UNIT 7

adore + -ing
bald
beard
black
blonde
brown
can't stand + -ing
cheerful
clever
crazy about
curly
dark
don´t mind + -ing
enjoy + -ing
fair
fond of
freckles
friendly
funny
glasses
(not) good at
grey
hate + -ing
interested at
into
keen on
(don't) like + -ing
long
love + -ing
medium height
moustache

piercing
plump
red
serious
short
shy
slim
straight
tall
terrible at
wavy
well-built

UNIT 8

accountant
architect
builder
bus driver
business person
clean the car
clear the table
do the ironing
do the vacuuming
do the washing
do the washing up
doctor
engineer
farmer
feed the dog
firefighter
hang out the washing
lawyer
lay the table
load the dishwasher
make the bed
manager
nurse
pilot
plumber
police officer
put away the groceries
sales representative
shop assistant
sweep the floor
take out the rubbish
take the dog for a walk
university professor
vet
water the plants

UNIT 9

art gallery
bank
blu-ray disc player
bookshop
camcorder
cinema
coffee shop
department store
digital camera
hard drive
high-definition TV
hotel
internet café
library
microphone
mouse
MP3 dock
multi card reader
museum
newsagents
park
pharmacy
police station
printer
remote control
restaurant
sandwich bar
satellite speakers
shopping centre
sports centre
stadium
supermarket
surround sound
theatre
town hall
USB port
webcam
widescreen
wireless keyboard

IDEAS

1 **Read the story *Ideas* on pages 130-131 of your Student's Book again. Then complete the summary of the story with your own ideas.**

This story is set in ________________. The main characters are ________________________________.

At the start of the story, Ruby ________________________.
She's doing this because ________________________.

Suddenly, she ________________________.
After that, ________________________.

In the end, ________________________.

I thought this story was ________________ because ________________________________.

2 **Write ten words and expressions from the story that you want to learn. Write a record so that you remember them.**

____
____
____
____
____
____
____
____
____
____

WHITE

1 **Read the story *White* on pages 132–133 of your Student's Book again. Then complete the summary of the story with your own ideas.**

This story is set in ________________. The main characters are ________________________________.

At the start of the story, Jacob ________________________.
The next morning, ________________________.

Suddenly, ________________________
________________________________.

In the end, ________________________.

I thought this story was ________________ because ________________________________.

2 **Write ten words and expressions from the story that you want to learn. Write a record so that you remember them.**

____
____
____
____
____
____
____
____
____
____

THREE PLUS ONE

1 **Read the story *Three plus one* on pages 134–135 of your Student's Book again. Then complete the summary of the story with your own ideas.**

The main characters of this story are ________________________________.

Jamie and his friends ________________________.
At the start of the story, Jamie ________________________.

In the Maths lesson, ________________________
________________________________.

After that, ________________________
________________________________.

In the end, ________________________.

I thought this story was ________________ because ________________________________.

2 **Write ten words and expressions from the story that you want to learn. Write a record so that you remember them.**

____
____
____
____
____
____
____
____
____
____